This revision and classroom companion is matched to the new single award AQA GCSE Chemistry specification. It provides full coverage of the three units of substantive content (scientific explanations and evidence) and the procedural content, How Science Works, which is explained thoroughly on pages 4–11.

For each sub-section of substantive content, the AQA GCSE Chemistry specification identifies activities you should be able to complete using your skills, knowledge and understanding of how science works. Many of these activities focus on issues that highlight the role of science in society and the impact it has on our lives, and require you to evaluate information, develop arguments and draw conclusions.

The activities are dealt with in this guide on the How Science Works pages (picked out with shaded backgrounds), which are integrated into the three main units. The points identified on these pages are designed to provide a starting point, from which you can begin to develop your own conclusions. They are not meant to be definitive or prescriptive.

At the end of each unit you will find a page of exam-style questions complete with model answers, to help you understand what is expected of you in the exam. Unit 1 features a combination of multiple choice questions and longer structured questions to reflect the different methods of assessment; Unit 2 and Unit 3 just have structured questions.

At the end of each unit there is also a page of key words and their meanings. These pages can be used as checklists to help you with your revision. Make sure you are familiar with all the words listed and understand their meanings and relevance – they are central to your understanding of the material in that unit!

Throughout this volume, material which is higher tier only appears within a box with a grey background.

This companion is intended as a source of first-rate revision material for GCSE students; but it is our hope that it will also ease the burden of over-worked science departments.

How to Use

This revision and everything you format. In certai more than the s know to aid understanding.

Don't just read the book: learn actively! Constantly test yourself without looking at the text. Jot down anything you think will help you to remember – no matter how trivial it may seem.

About the Author

In her 30 years as a science teacher, **Christine Horbury** worked with students of all abilities, including children with special needs and gifted and talented pupils. As a science consultant for an LEA she works closely with the exam boards and has an excellent understanding of the new science specifications, which she is helping to implement in local schools.

Published by Lonsdale, a division of Huveaux PLC.

Acknowledgements

p.3	©iStockphoto.com / Andrei Tchernov
p.5	©iStockphoto.com / Audrey Roorda
p.6	©iStockphoto.com / Todd Smith
p.7	©iStockphoto.com / James Antrim
p.16	©iStockphoto.com / Don Wilkie
p.21	©iStockphoto.com / Duncan Walker
p.24	©iStockphoto.com / Laurin Rinder
p.28	©iStockphoto.com / Jim Parkin
p.29	©iStockphoto.com / Sean Fishlock
p.29	©iStockphoto.com / Stephan Kohler
p.57	©iStockphoto.com / Jean Schweitzer
p.61	©iStockphoto.com / Viktor Pryymachuk
p.61	©iStockphoto.com / Mark Evans
p.66	©iStockphoto.com / Jon Kroninger

Contents

Contents

The numbers in brackets correspond to the reference numbers on the AQA GCSE Chemistry specification.

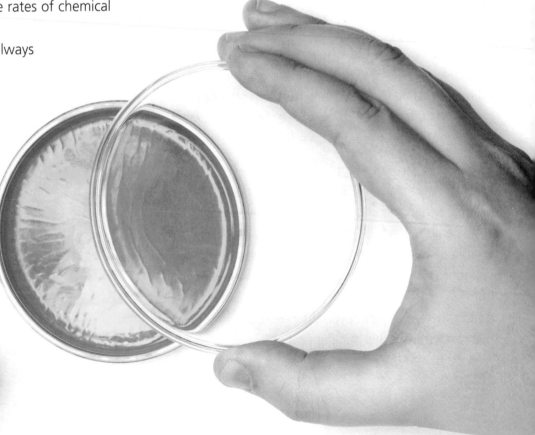

How Science Works

The new AQA GCSE Chemistry specification incorporates two types of content:

- **Science Content** (example shown opposite)
  This is all the scientific explanations and evidence that you need to be able to recall in your exams (objective tests or written exams). It is covered on pages 12–101 of the revision guide.

- **How Science Works** (example shown opposite)
  This is a set of key concepts, relevant to all areas of science. It is concerned with how scientific evidence is obtained and the effect it has on society. More specifically, it covers…

  - the relationship between scientific evidence and scientific explanations and theories
  - the practices and procedures used to collect scientific evidence
  - the reliability and validity of scientific evidence
  - the role of science in society and the impact it has on our lives
  - how decisions are made about the use of science and technology in different situations, and the factors affecting these decisions.

Because they are interlinked, your teacher will have taught the two types of content together in your science lessons. Likewise, the questions on your exam papers are likely to combine elements from both types of content, i.e. to answer them, you will need to recall the relevant scientific facts *and* draw upon your knowledge of how science works.

The key concepts from How Science Works are summarised in this section of the revision guide. You should be familiar with all of them, especially the practices and procedures used to collect scientific data (from all your practical investigations). But make sure you work through them all. Make a note if there is anything you are unsure about and then ask your teacher for clarification.

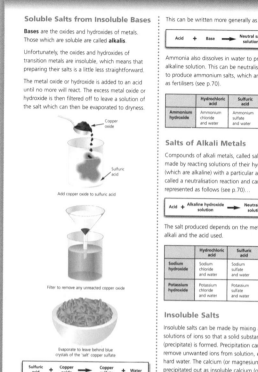

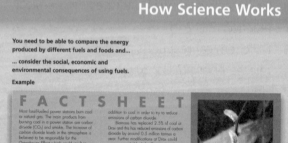

How to Use This Revision Guide

The AQA GCSE Chemistry specification includes activities for each sub-section of science content, which require you to apply your knowledge of how science works, to help develop your skills when it comes to evaluating information, developing arguments and drawing conclusions.

These activities are dealt with on the How Science Works pages (on a tinted background) throughout the revision guide. Make sure you work through them all, as questions relating to the skills, ideas and issues covered on these pages could easily come up in the exam. Bear in mind that these pages are designed to provide a starting point from which you can begin to develop your own ideas and conclusions. They are not meant to be definitive or prescriptive.

Practical tips on how to evaluate information are included in this section, on page 11.

What is the Purpose of Science?

Science attempts to explain the world we live in. The role of a scientist is to collect evidence through investigations to...

- explain phenomena (e.g. explain how and why something happens)
- solve problems.

Scientific knowledge and understanding can lead to the development of new technologies (e.g. in medicine and industry) which have a huge impact on society and the environment.

Scientific Evidence

The purpose of evidence is to provide facts which answer a specific question, and therefore support or disprove an idea or theory. In science, evidence is often based on data that has been collected by making observations and measurements.

To allow scientists to reach appropriate conclusions, evidence must be...

- **reliable**, i.e. it must be reproducible by others and therefore be trustworthy
- **valid**, i.e. it must be reliable and it must answer the question.

N.B. If data is not reliable, it cannot be valid.

To ensure scientific evidence is reliable and valid, scientists employ a range of ideas and practices which relate to...

1 **observations** – how we observe the world
2 **investigations** – designing investigations so that patterns and relationships can be identified
3 **measurements** – making measurements by selecting and using instruments effectively
4 **presenting data** – presenting and representing data
5 **conclusions** – identifying patterns and relationships and making suitable conclusions.

These five key ideas are covered in more detail on the following pages.

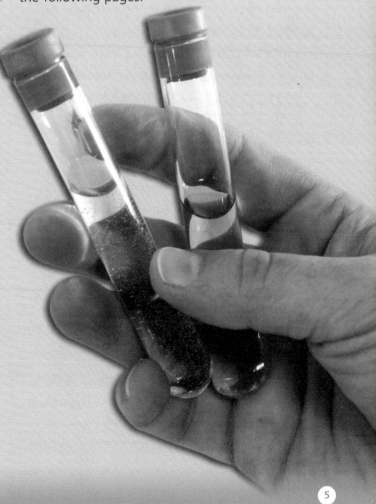

How Science Works

① Observations

Most scientific investigations begin with an observation, i.e. a scientist observes an event or phenomenon and decides to find out more about how and why it happens.

The first step is to develop a **hypothesis**, i.e. to *suggest* an explanation for the phenomenon. Hypotheses normally propose a relationship between two or more variables (factors that change). They are based on careful observations and existing scientific knowledge, and often include a bit of creative thinking.

The hypothesis is used to make a prediction, which can be tested through scientific investigation. The data collected during the investigation might support the hypothesis, show it to be untrue, or lead to the development of a new hypothesis.

Example

A biologist **observes** that freshwater shrimp are only found in certain parts of a stream.

He uses current scientific knowledge of shrimp behaviour and water flow to develop a **hypothesis**, which relates the distribution of shrimp (first variable) to the rate of water flow (second variable).

Based on this hypothesis, the biologist **predicts** that shrimp can only be found in areas of the stream where the flow rate is beneath a certain value.

The prediction is **investigated** through a survey, which looks for the presence of shrimp in different parts of the stream, representing a range of different flow rates.

The **data** shows that shrimp are only present in parts of the stream where the flow rate is below a certain value (i.e. it supports the hypothesis). However, it also shows that shrimp are not *always* present in parts of the stream where the flow rate is below this value.

As a result, the biologist realises there must be another factor affecting the distribution of shrimp. So, he **refines his hypothesis**, to relate the distribution of shrimp (first variable) to the concentration of oxygen in the water (second variable) in parts of the stream where there is a slow flow rate.

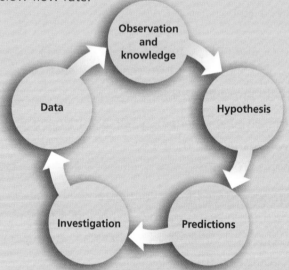

If new observations or data do not match existing explanations or theories, e.g. if unexpected behaviour is displayed, they need to be checked for reliability and validity.

In some cases it turns out that the new observations and data are valid, so existing theories and explanations have to be revised or amended. This is how scientific knowledge gradually grows and develops.

❷ Investigations

An investigation involves collecting data to try to determine whether there is a relationship between two variables. A variable is any factor that can take different values (i.e. change). In an investigation you have two variables:

- **independent variable**, which is controlled or known by the person carrying out the investigation. In the shrimp example on page 6, the independent variable is the flow rate of the water.
- **dependent variable**, which is measured each time a change is made to the independent variable, to see if it also changes. In the shrimp example on page 6, the dependent variable is the distribution of shrimp (i.e. whether shrimp are present or not).

Variables can have different types of values...

- **continuous variables** – can take any numerical values. These are usually measurements, e.g. temperature or height.
- **discrete variables** – can only take whole-number values. These are usually quantities, e.g. the number of shrimp in a population.
- **ordered variables** – have relative values, e.g. small, medium or large.
- **categoric variables** – have a limited number of specific values, e.g. the different breeds of dog: dalmatian, cocker spaniel, labrador etc.

Numerical values tend to be more powerful and informative than ordered variables and categoric variables.

An investigation tries to establish whether an observed link between two variables is...

- **causal** – a change in one variable causes a change in the other, e.g. in a chemical reaction the rate of reaction (dependent variable) increases when the temperature of the reactants (independent variable) is increased
- **due to association** – the changes in the two variables are linked by a third variable, e.g. a link between the change in pH of a stream (first variable) and a change in the number of different species found in the stream (second variable), may be the effect of a change in the concentration of atmospheric pollutants (third variable)
- **due to chance** – the change in the two variables is unrelated; it is coincidental, e.g. in the 1940s the number of deaths due to lung cancer increased as did the amount of tar being used in road construction, however, one *did not* cause the other.

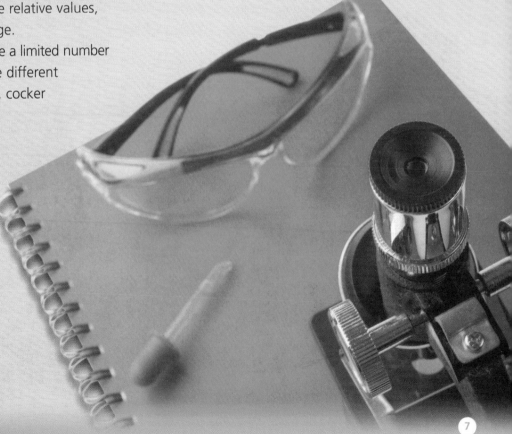

How Science Works

Fair Test

A fair test is one in which the only factor that can affect the dependent variable is the independent variable. Any other variables (outside variables) that could influence the results are kept the same.

This is a lot easier in the laboratory than in the field, where conditions (e.g. weather) cannot always be physically controlled. The impact of outside variables, like the weather, has to be reduced by ensuring all measurements are affected by the variable in the same way. For example, if you were investigating the effect of different fertilisers on the growth of tomato plants, all the plants would need to be grown in a place where they were subject to the same weather conditions.

If a survey is used to collect data, the impact of outside variables can be reduced by ensuring that the individuals in the sample are closely matched. For example, if you were investigating the effect of smoking on life expectancy, the individuals in the sample would all need to have a similar diet and lifestyle to ensure that those variables do not affect the results.

Control groups are often used in biological research. For example, in some drugs trials, a placebo (a dummy pill containing no medicine) is given to one group of volunteers – the control group – and the drug is given to another. By comparing the two groups, scientists can establish whether the drug (the independent variable) is the only variable affecting the volunteers and, therefore, whether it is a fair test.

Accuracy and Precision

In an investigation, the mean (average) of a set of repeated measurements is often calculated to overcome small variations and get a best estimate of the true value. Increasing the number of measurements taken will improve the accuracy and the reliability of their mean.

$$\text{Mean} = \frac{\text{Sum of all measurements}}{\text{Number of measurements}}$$

The purpose of an investigation will determine how accurate the data collected needs to be. For example, measures of blood alcohol levels must be accurate enough to determine whether a person is legally fit to drive.

The data collected must also be precise enough to form a valid conclusion, i.e. it should provide clear evidence for or against the hypothesis.

Fertiliser 1

Fertiliser 2

Fertiliser 3

③ Measurements

Even if all outside variables have been controlled, there are certain factors that could still affect the reliability and validity of any measurements made:

- **the accuracy of the instruments used** – The accuracy of a measuring instrument will depend on how accurately it has been calibrated. Expensive equipment is likely to be more accurately calibrated.
- **the sensitivity of the instruments used** – The sensitivity of an instrument is determined by the smallest change in value it can detect. For example, bathroom scales are not sensitive enough to detect the changes in weight of a small baby, whereas the scales used by a midwife to monitor growth are.
- **human error** – When making measurements, random errors can occur due to a lapse in concentration and systematic (repeated) errors can occur if the instrument has not been calibrated properly or is continuously misused.

Any anomalous (irregular) values, e.g. values that fall well outside the range (the spread) of the other measurements, need to be examined to try to determine the cause. If they have been caused by an equipment failure or human error, it is common practice to ignore such values and discount them from any following calculations.

> **Range** **=** **Maximum value** **−** **Minimum value**

④ Presenting Data

Data is often presented in a format that makes the patterns more evident. This makes it easier to see the relationship between two variables. The relationship between variables can be linear (positive or negative) or directly proportional.

Clear presentation of data also makes it easier to identify any anomalous values.

The type of chart or graph used to present data will depend on the type of variable involved.

Tables organise data (patterns and anomalies in the data are not always obvious).

Height (cm)	127	165	149	147	155	161	154	138	145
Shoe size	5	8	5	6	5	5	6	4	5

Bar charts are used to display data when the independent variable is categoric or discrete and the dependent variable is continuous.

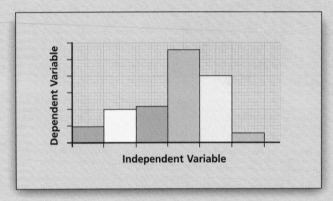

Line graphs are used to display data when both variables are continuous.

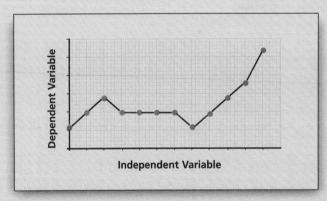

Scattergrams (or scatter diagrams) are used to show the underlying relationship between two variables. This can be made clearer by including a line of best fit.

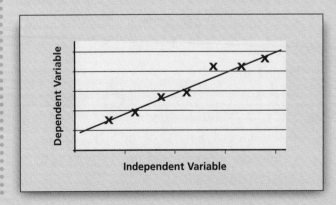

How Science Works

⑤ Conclusions

Conclusions should...
- describe the patterns and relationships between variables
- take all the data into account
- make direct reference to the original hypothesis /prediction.

Conclusions should not...
- be influenced by anything other than the data collected
- disregard any data (other than anomalous values)
- include any speculation.

Evaluation

An evaluation looks at the investigation as a whole. It should consider...
- the original purpose of the investigation
- the appropriateness of the methods and techniques used

- the reliability and validity of the data
- the validity of the conclusions (e.g. whether the original purpose was achieved).

The reliability of an investigation can be increased by...
- looking at relevant data from secondary sources
- using an alternative method to check results
- ensuring that the results can be reproduced by others.

Science and Society

Scientific understanding can lead to technological developments, which can be exploited by different groups of people for different reasons. For example, the successful development of a new drug benefits the drugs company financially and improves the quality of life for patients.

The applications of scientific and technological developments can raise certain issues. An issue is an important question that is in dispute and needs to be settled. Decisions made by individuals and society about these issues may not be based on scientific evidence alone.

Social issues are concerned with the impact on the human population of a community, city, country, or even the world.

Economic issues are concerned with money and related factors like employment and the distribution of resources. There is often an overlap between social and economic issues.

Environmental issues are concerned with the impact on the planet; its natural ecosystems and resources.

Ethical issues are concerned with what is morally right and wrong, i.e. they require a value judgement to be made about what is acceptable. As society is underpinned by a common belief system; there are certain actions that can never be justified. However, because the views of individuals are influenced by lots of different factors (e.g. faith and personal experience) there are also lots of grey areas.

Evaluating Information

It is important that you can evaluate information relating to social-scientific issues. You could be asked to do this in the exam, but it will also help you make informed decisions in life (e.g. decide whether or not to have a particular vaccination or become involved in a local recycling campaign).

When you are asked to **evaluate** information, start by making a list of the pluses and the minuses. Then work through the two lists, and for each point consider how this might impact on society. Remember, **PMI** – pluses, minuses, impact on society.

You also need to be sure that the source of information is reliable and credible. Here are some important factors to consider:

- **opinion**
  Opinions are personal viewpoints. Opinions which are backed up by valid and reliable evidence carry far more weight than those based on non-scientific ideas (e.g. hearsay or urban myths).

- **bias**
  Information is biased if it does not provide a balanced account; it favours a particular viewpoint. Biased information might include incomplete evidence or try to influence how you interpret the evidence. For example, a drugs company might highlight the benefits of their drugs but downplay the side-effects in order to increase sales.

- **weight of evidence**
  Scientific evidence can be given undue weight or dismissed too lightly due to...
  - political significance, e.g. evidence that is likely to provoke an extreme and negative reaction from the public might be downplayed
  - status (academic or professional status, experience, authority and reputation), e.g. evidence is likely to be given more weight if it comes from someone who is a recognised expert in that particular field.

Limitations of Science

Science can help us in lots of ways but it cannot supply all the answers. We are still finding out about things and developing our scientific knowledge. There are some questions that we cannot answer, maybe because we do not have enough reliable and valid evidence.

There are some questions that science cannot answer at all. These tend to be questions relating to ethical issues, where beliefs and opinions are important, or to situations where we cannot collect reliable and valid scientific evidence. In other words, science can often tell us whether something *can* be done and *how* it can be done, but it cannot tell us whether it *should* be done.

Unit 1

11.1

How do rocks provide building materials?

Industry makes use of naturally occurring rock to provide essential building materials. Limestone is used in the manufacture of cement, concrete and glass. To understand this, you need to know...

- what atoms and elements are
- how elements are arranged in the periodic table
- what a compound is and how it is formed
- why limestone is a useful resource
- how limestone is used to produce building materials.

Atoms

All substances are made of **atoms** (very small particles). Each atom has a small central **nucleus** made up of **protons** and **neutrons** that is surrounded by **electrons**.

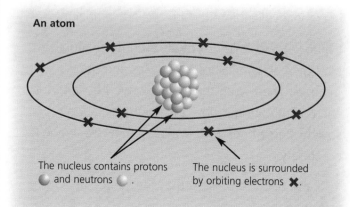

An atom

The nucleus contains protons and neutrons .

The nucleus is surrounded by orbiting electrons ✗.

Elements

A substance which contains only one sort of atom is called an **element**. There are about 100 different elements.

The atoms of each element are represented by a different chemical symbol, for example, O for oxygen, Na for sodium, C for carbon, and Fe for iron. Elements are arranged in the periodic table (see below). The groups in the periodic table contain elements that have similar properties.

Compounds

Compounds are substances in which the atoms of two or more elements are chemically combined, i.e. the atoms are held together by **chemical bonds** (not just mixed together).

When elements react, the atoms can form chemical bonds by...

- sharing electrons
- giving or taking electrons.

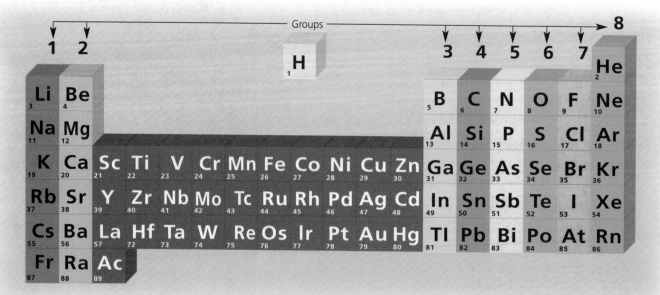

Chemical Formulae

Compounds are represented by a combination of numbers and chemical symbols called a **formula**, e.g. ZnO or $2H_2SO_4$.

Chemists use formulae to show...
- the different elements in a compound
- the ratio of atoms of each element in the compound.

In chemical formulae, the position of the numbers tells you what is multiplied. Smaller numbers that sit below the line (subscripts) only multiply the symbol that comes immediately before it, and large numbers that are the same size as the letters multiply all the symbols that come after,
e.g. H_2O means (2 x H) + (1 x O)
     2NaOH means 2 x (NaOH) or 2 x (Na + O + H).

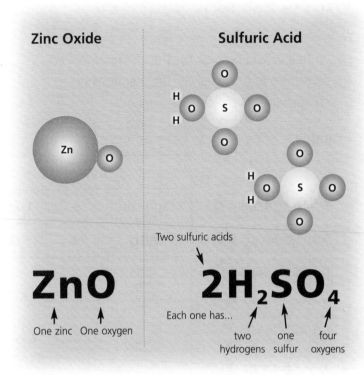

Zinc Oxide

ZnO
One zinc   One oxygen

Sulfuric Acid

Two sulfuric acids

$2H_2SO_4$

Each one has...
two hydrogens   one sulfur   four oxygens

Chemical Reactions

You can show what has happened during a reaction by writing a **word equation** with the substances that react (the **reactants**) on one side of the equation and the new substances formed (the **products**) on the other.

The total mass of the products of a chemical reaction is always equal to the total mass of the reactants.

This is because the products of a chemical reaction are made up from exactly the same atoms as the reactants – no atoms are lost or made!

That means chemical symbol equations must always be balanced: there must be the same number of atoms of each element on the reactant side of the equation as there is on the product side.

Example

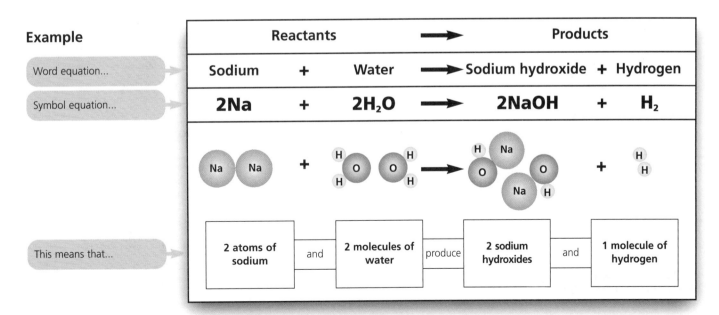

	Reactants	→	Products
Word equation...	Sodium + Water →		Sodium hydroxide + Hydrogen
Symbol equation...	2Na + $2H_2O$ →		2NaOH + H_2

This means that... | 2 atoms of sodium | and | 2 molecules of water | produce | 2 sodium hydroxides | and | 1 molecule of hydrogen |

Unit 1

Writing Balanced Equations

Follow these steps to write a balanced equation:

1. write a word equation for the chemical reaction
2. substitute in formulae for the elements or compounds involved
3. balance the equation by adding numbers in front of the reactants and / or products
4. write down a balanced symbol equation (see p.13).

Example 1 – The reaction between magnesium and oxygen.

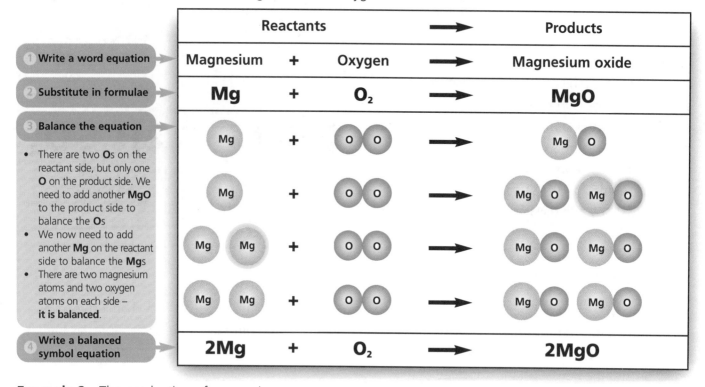

Example 2 - The production of ammonia.

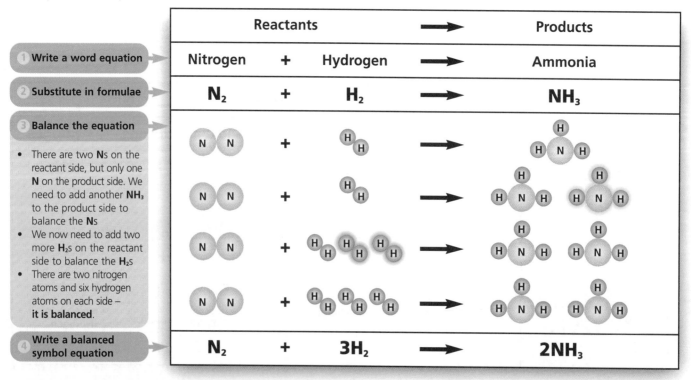

Limestone

Limestone is a sedimentary rock which consists mainly of the compound **calcium carbonate**. It is cheap, easy to obtain and has many uses.

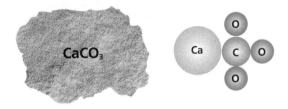

1 Building Material

Limestone can be **quarried** and cut into blocks, and used to build walls of houses in regions where it is plentiful.

Over time it can be eroded by acid rain, but this is a very slow process.

2 Neutralising Agent

Alkalis in soil can be 'washed out' by acid rain. Excess acidity in soils can cause crop failure. Powdered limestone can correct this but it works quite slowly.

When calcium carbonate is heated in a kiln it decomposes. This reaction is called **thermal decomposition** and it causes the calcium carbonate to break down into **calcium oxide (quicklime)** and **carbon dioxide**. Carbonates of other metals decompose in a similar way.

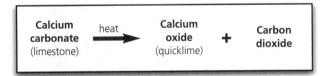

The calcium oxide (quicklime) can then be reacted (slaked) with water to produce **calcium hydroxide (slaked lime)**.

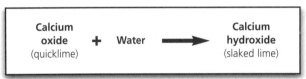

Calcium hydroxide (like all hydroxides), is a strong **alkali**. It can be used to neutralise soils and lakes much faster than powdered limestone. *N.B. The carbonates of other metals behave very similarly when they are heated.*

3 Glass

Glass is made by mixing powdered limestone, sand and soda (sodium carbonate) and heating the mixture until it melts. When cool, it is transparent.

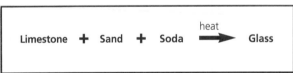

4 Cement, Mortar and Concrete

Powdered limestone and powdered clay are roasted in a rotary kiln to produce dry **cement**.

When the cement is mixed with sand and water it produces **mortar**, which is used to hold together bricks and stone during building.

When the cement is mixed with water, sand and gravel (crushed rock) a slow reaction takes place where a hard, stone-like building material, called **concrete**, is produced.

How Science Works

You need to be able to consider and evaluate the environmental, social and economic effects of exploiting limestone and producing building materials from it.

Advantages	Disadvantages
• Limestone is found naturally, so can be quarried relatively easily. • Using local stone to build new houses makes them 'fit in' with older houses. • Better roads will be built to cope with quarry traffic. • Creates more jobs locally. • Other industries (e.g. cement makers) will be attracted to the area, providing more job opportunities. • The quarry might invest in the local community in a bid to 'win over' the locals.	• Could be more expensive to quarry limestone than to use another building material. • Quarries destroy the landscape and the habitats of animals and birds. • Increased traffic to and from the quarries. • Noise pollution. • Health problems arising from the dust particles, e.g. asthma. • Reduced tourism in the area.

You need to be able to evaluate the advantages and disadvantages of using limestone, concrete and glass as building materials.

Material	Advantages	Disadvantages
Limestone	• Widely available. • Easy to cut. • Cheaper than many other building materials, e.g. marble. • Can be used to produce cement, concrete and glass.	• Susceptible to acid rain – the dilute acid dissolves the limestone very slowly, wearing it away.
Concrete	• Can be moulded into different shapes, e.g. panels and blocks which can be put together easily in buildings. • Quick and cheap way to construct buildings. • Does not corrode, so is a good alternative to metal. • Can be reinforced using steel bars so that it is safer and has a wider range of uses.	• Low tensile strength* and can crack and become dangerous, especially in high-rise buildings. • Looks unattractive.
Glass	• Transparent, therefore useful for windows and parts of buildings where natural light is wanted. • Can be toughened or made into safety glass.	• Breaks easily. • Not always the cheapest or safest option.

All of these materials are resistant to fire and rot, and are strong enough to resist attack from animals and insects, which make them a better choice than wood. However, there may be cheaper, safer and more aesthetically pleasing materials that are also suitable for the job.

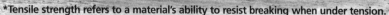

*Tensile strength refers to a material's ability to resist breaking when under tension.

11.2

How do rocks provide metals and how are metals used?

Metals have lots of uses in our homes, workplaces and environment. Metals begin life as an ore: a naturally occurring mineral (or rock). To understand how these rocks provide metals and how we then use them, you need to know...

- what an ore is
- how we obtain different metals (reactive and unreactive)
- what properties and uses different metals have.

Ores

The Earth's crust contains many naturally occurring elements and compounds called **minerals**. A metal **ore** is a mineral or mixture of minerals from which economically viable amounts of pure metal can be **extracted**. This can change over time.

Extracting Metals from their Ores

The method of extraction depends on how reactive the metal is. Unreactive metals like gold exist naturally. They are obtained through physical processes such as panning.

Most metals are found as **metal oxides** or compounds that can be easily changed into a metal oxide. To extract a metal from its oxide the oxygen must be removed by heating the oxide with another element in a chemical reaction. This process is called **reduction**.

Metals that are less reactive than carbon can be extracted from their oxides by heating them with carbon. (The carbon is a more reactive element, so it will displace the metal and form a compound with the oxygen.)

Iron

Iron oxide can be reduced in a blast furnace to produce iron.

Molten **iron** obtained from a blast furnace contains roughly 96% iron, and 4% carbon and other metals. Because it is impure, the iron is very brittle with limited uses. To produce **pure iron**, all the impurities would have to be removed.

The atoms in pure iron are arranged in layers, which can slide over each other easily. This makes pure iron soft and malleable – it can be easily shaped. However, it is too soft for many practical uses.

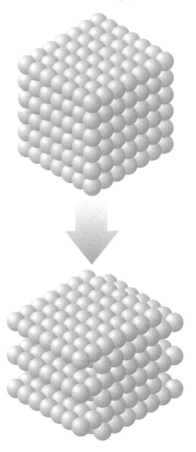

The properties of iron can be changed by mixing it with small quantities of carbon or other metals to make **steel**, which is an **alloy**.

Alloys

An alloy is a mixture which contains a metal and at least one other element. The added element disturbs the regular arrangement of the metal atoms so that the layers do not slide over each other so easily. Alloys are, therefore, usually stronger and harder than pure metals. Many of the metals we use everyday are alloys.

Pure copper, gold and aluminium are too soft for many uses. They are mixed with small amounts of similar metals to make them harder for everyday use.

Steel

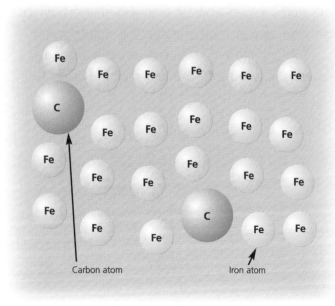

Carbon atom   Iron atom

Carbon is added to iron to make the alloy steel. A majority of iron is converted into steel.

To make steel, the molten iron from a blast furnace is transferred into another furnace. Here it is mixed with recycled scrap metal and pure oxygen is passed into the mixture. The oxygen reacts with the non-metal impurities such as carbon, silicon and sulfur to produce acidic oxides.

Alloys like steel are developed to have the necessary properties for a specific purpose. In steel, the amount of carbon and/or other elements determines its properties:

- steel with a high carbon content is hard and strong, e.g. screwdrivers
- steel with a low carbon content is soft and easily shaped. Mild steel (0.25% carbon) is easily pressed into shape, e.g. cars
- steel which contains chromium and nickel is called stainless steel. It is hard and resistant to corrosion, e.g. knives and forks.

Smart Alloys

Smart alloys belong to a group of materials that are being developed to meet the demands of modern engineering and manufacturing. These materials respond to changes in their environment, e.g. temperature, moisture, pH and electrical and magnetic fields.

Smart alloys (also called shape memory alloys) remember their shape. They can be deformed, but will return to their original shape (usually when they are heated).

Alloys of nickel-titanium, silver-cadmium, copper-aluminium-nickel and copper-zinc-aluminium can possess the shape memory effect. They are useful in thermostats; car, plane and helicopter parts; and flexible spectacle frames.

The Transition Metals

In the centre of the **periodic table**, between Group 2 and Group 3, is a block of metallic elements called the **transition metals**. These include: iron, copper, platinum, mercury, chromium, titanium and zinc.

These metals are **hard** and mechanically **strong**. They have **high melting points** (except mercury – which is liquid at room temperature).

Transition metals, like all other metals, are **good conductors** of heat and electricity, and can also be easily bent or hammered into shape.

These properties make transition metals very useful as structural materials, and as electrical and thermal conductors.

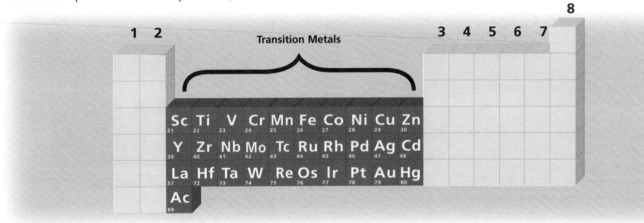

Extracting Transition Metals

Copper, aluminium and titanium, unlike iron, cannot be extracted from their ores by reduction with carbon. They are extracted through a process called **electrolysis**.

Electrolysis is very complex – there are lots of different stages – and requires a large amount of energy. This makes it very expensive. So, we should recycle metals wherever possible to…
* save money and energy
* make sure we do not use up all the natural resources
* reduce the amount of mining because it is damaging the environment.

Copper

Copper is useful for **electrical wiring** and **plumbing** but natural supplies of ores containing large quantities of copper are limited. If we continue to use them they will run out completely.

Scientists are trying to find ways to extract copper from other ores which contain less copper but are more abundant.

Aluminium

Aluminium is **resistant to corrosion**. A reaction between the aluminium and oxygen from the air produces a thin 'skin' which prevents further corrosion. It is for this reason that greenhouses do not have to be painted. However, for some uses of aluminium, a thicker layer of this protective oxide is needed.

Aluminium has a **low density** so it is very light. It is used for…
* drinks cans
* window frames
* lightweight vehicles
* aeroplanes.

Titanium

Titanium is **strong** and **resistant to corrosion**. It is used in…
* aeroplanes
* nuclear reactors
* replacement hip joints.

How Science Works

You need to be able to consider and evaluate the social, economic and environmental impacts of exploiting metal ores, of using metals and of recycling metals.

Example

Local Village Launches National Campaign

The villagers of Littlehampton are speaking out to show us all how we can help to reduce the damage being done to our environment.

A large metal extraction plant was built near Littlehampton 15 years ago and the village has suffered from the effects of the industry ever since. The plant has had a detrimental impact not only on the look of the area but also on its environment. The pollution has made its way into rivers and streams, and the local wildlife group reports that certain species are dwindling in number.

These bad effects are not only limited to wildlife. The noise that comes from the factory is annoying, but more worrying is the dramatic increase in the number of local people who suffer from asthma as a result of the dust particles discharged into the air.

Now, after proposals to extend the plant have been revealed, villagers have joined together to recycle metals and want to encourage others to do the same. Campaign spokesman, Bob Jeffries, 42, says, 'We know that metals are useful materials and that extraction needs to be done, but we hope to encourage people to recycle what they can. This should reduce the demand for newly extracted metals and remove the need for new plants. Not only will we be improving our standard of living but we will also be helping to reduce the pressure and impact on our environment'.

Recycling is a much better option because it uses less energy, which makes it a much cheaper process. The more times a material is recycled, the more cost-effective it becomes.

Councillors listened to the views of local residents and agreed to implement a recycling scheme. Five large recycling bins have been brought in to the car park at the local supermarket. Said councillor Cilla Jackson, 56, 'The scheme has had a much better response than we had hoped for; I just hope the enthusiasm for it is maintained'. *For information on how you can do your bit go to www.recyclenow.com*

Method	Advantages	Disadvantages
Extracting metals	• Provides jobs and income locally. • Provides raw materials for industry. • Local facilities (e.g. roads) will be improved to cope with additional traffic.	• Destroys the landscape. • Leads to a reduction in tourism. • Noise and dust pollution. • Traffic problems.
Recycling metals	• Saves energy (e.g. less energy used to recycle aluminium than to electrolyse the ore it comes from). • Less pollution produced because fewer materials are sent to landfill sites. • Less pressure placed on environment (the more material that is recycled, the less pressure there is to find new materials to mine, extract, etc.).	• Individual apathy. • Availability and collection of recycling facilities.

How Science Works

You need to be able to evaluate the advantages and disadvantages of using metals as structural materials and as smart materials.

Use of Metal	Advantages	Disadvantages
Structural material	• Hard, tough and strong. • Do not corrode easily. • Can be bent or hammered into shape. • Alloys of metals are harder than pure metals.	• Iron is naturally very soft so needs to be mixed with other metals to form steel. • Conduct electricity and heat – this might not be what is wanted. • Some metals, particularly iron, can be corroded by water and other chemicals – this weakens and eventually wears away the metal. • The supply of metal ores from the Earth's crust is decreasing as more is extracted – eventually the supplies will run out.
Smart material	• Can be produced by mixing metals which have many advantageous properties over the original metals. • Good mechanical properties, e.g. strong and resist corrosion. • Can return to their original shape when heated (known as the shape-memory effect) – used in thermostats, coffee pots, hydraulic fittings. • More bendy than normal metals, therefore harder to damage. • Have new properties, such as pseudo-elasticity, which can be exploited in diverse ways, such as in glasses frames, bra underwires and orthodontic arches. • Can be changed by passing an electrical current or a magnetic field through them or by heating. • Not much temperature change required (sometimes as little as 10°C) to change the molecular structure.	• Expensive to manufacture. • Fatigue easily – a steel component can survive for around 100 times longer than a smart material under the same pressure.

Unit 1

How do we get fuels from crude oil?

Crude oil is found in rocks and can be used to produce fuels. To understand this, you need to know...

- the difference between a compound and a mixture
- how crude oil can be fractionally distilled to produce fuels
- that most fuels contain carbon and hydrogen and sometimes sulfur
- what happens when fuels are burned; the effect that sulfur has on the environment.

Crude Oil

Crude oil is a mixture of compounds, most of which are molecules made up of carbon and hydrogen atoms only, called **hydrocarbons**. These hydrocarbon molecules vary in size. This affects their properties and how they are used as fuels. The larger the hydrocarbon (i.e. the greater the number of carbon and hydrogen atoms in a molecule)...

- the less easily it flows, i.e. the more viscous it is
- the less easily it ignites, i.e. the less flammable it is
- the less volatile it is, i.e. it doesn't vaporise as easily
- the higher its boiling point.

Short-chain hydrocarbon

Long-chain hydrocarbon

A **mixture** consists of two or more elements or compounds which are not chemically combined together, so the properties of the substances in the mixture remain unchanged and specific to that substance. This makes it possible to separate the substances in a mixture by physical methods such as **distillation**.

Fractional Distillation

Crude oil on its own is not very useful. However, different hydrocarbons have different boiling points which means that crude oil can be separated into different parts, or **fractions**, by **fractional distillation**. Most of the hydrocarbons obtained are alkanes (see p.23).

In fractional distillation, the oil is evaporated (by heating) and then allowed to condense at a range of different temperatures. This is when it forms fractions, each of which contains hydrocarbon molecules with a similar number of carbon atoms. This is done in a fractionating column (see below).

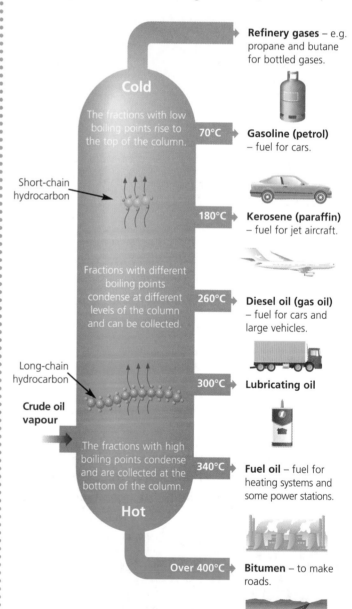

Refinery gases – e.g. propane and butane for bottled gases.

Cold

The fractions with low boiling points rise to the top of the column.

Short-chain hydrocarbon

70°C — **Gasoline (petrol)** – fuel for cars.

180°C — **Kerosene (paraffin)** – fuel for jet aircraft.

Fractions with different boiling points condense at different levels of the column and can be collected.

260°C — **Diesel oil (gas oil)** – fuel for cars and large vehicles.

Long-chain hydrocarbon

300°C — **Lubricating oil**

Crude oil vapour

The fractions with high boiling points condense and are collected at the bottom of the column.

340°C — **Fuel oil** – fuel for heating systems and some power stations.

Hot

Over 400°C — **Bitumen** – to make roads.

Alkanes (Saturated Hydrocarbons)

The 'spine' of a hydrocarbon is made up of a chain of carbon atoms. When these are joined together by single carbon carbon bonds we say the hydrocarbon is saturated and it is known as an **alkane**. To put it simply…

- hydrogen atoms can make 1 bond each

- carbon atoms can make 4 bonds each

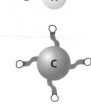
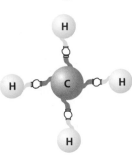

- the simplest alkane, methane, is made up of 4 hydrogen atoms and 1 carbon atom.

The general formula for alkanes is C_nH_{2n+2}. A more convenient way of representing alkanes is as follows…

Methane, CH_4

$$H - \overset{\displaystyle H}{\underset{\displaystyle H}{C}} - H$$

Ethane, C_2H_6

$$H - \overset{\displaystyle H}{\underset{\displaystyle H}{C}} - \overset{\displaystyle H}{\underset{\displaystyle H}{C}} - H$$

Propane, C_3H_8

$$H - \overset{\displaystyle H}{\underset{\displaystyle H}{C}} - \overset{\displaystyle H}{\underset{\displaystyle H}{C}} - \overset{\displaystyle H}{\underset{\displaystyle H}{C}} - H$$

In alkanes, all the carbon atoms are linked to 4 other atoms by single bonds. This means that all their bonds are 'occupied' (the alkane is saturated) so they are fairly unreactive, although they do burn well. The shorter-chain hydrocarbons release energy more quickly by burning, so there is a greater demand for them as fuels.

Burning Fuels

As fuels burn they produce waste products, which are then released into the atmosphere. The waste products produced depend on which elements are present in the fuel. Most fuels contain carbon and hydrogen, but many also contain some sulfur.

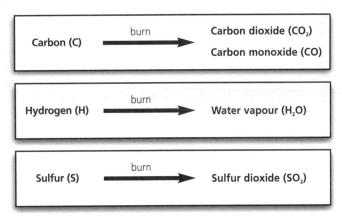

Carbon (C)	burn →	Carbon dioxide (CO_2) Carbon monoxide (CO)
Hydrogen (H)	burn →	Water vapour (H_2O)
Sulfur (S)	burn →	Sulfur dioxide (SO_2)

- CO_2 causes 'global warming' due to the Greenhouse Effect.
- SO_2 causes acid rain. Removing the sulfur before burning, or removing the SO_2 from the waste gases, can reduce this. However, both of these add to the cost.

Power stations remove sulfur dioxide from the waste gases produced when combustion takes place. This reduces the pollution they give out.

Particles may also be released in waste gases, which causes global dimming (a reduction in the amount of sunlight reaching the Earth's surface).

How Science Works

You need to be able to consider and evaluate the social, economic and environmental impacts of the uses of fuels.

Example

Forget Fossil Fuels...

When hydrocarbons are burned they release harmful waste gases into the air. Burning fossil fuels has a considerable impact on the environment and its inhabitants. The solution is to use fewer fossil fuels by using alternative energy resources, using existing resources more efficiently and by making changes to lifestyles, such as car-sharing to reduce fuel consumption, etc.

...Switch to Sugar!

Brazilian motorists have been converting their petrol-guzzling cars so they can be powered by ethanol. Ethanol, better known as grain alcohol, is easily distilled from sugar cane, and is a cheap alternative to petrol. This new use for sugar cane has greatly affected the farmers – never has there been such a high demand for sugar! This in turn has helped to push up the price of sugar to an all-time high. Scientists hope that the use of sugar cane as a viable alternative to petrol will grow, because it burns more cleanly than usual fuels and produces less of the harmful gas, carbon monoxide. However, it is not all good news. Alcohol releases less energy than petrol when it burns and it can be a health risk to filling station attendants.

You need to be able to evaluate developments in the production and uses of better fuels, for example, ethanol and hydrogen.

Example

Is Rocket Fuel the Way Forward?

Experts are carrying out research to find out if hydrogen gas, which is currently used as rocket fuel, could be an answer to our pollution problem. Hydrogen can be produced by passing an electric current through water, and when it burns it releases a lot of energy. Unlike other fuels which produce harmful gases when burnt, hydrogen produces only water vapour, which does not pollute the atmosphere. A major consideration is the costs involved because the production of hydrogen requires a lot of electricity. It could also be quite risky because hydrogen is flammable so it needs to be stored under special conditions.

Fuel	Advantages	Disadvantages
Fossil fuel	• Power stations provide jobs. • Provides energy for homes and industry. • Does not take up much space.	• Produces pollutants. • Causes global warming due to the Greenhouse Effect. • Non-renewable source so is in danger of running out.
Ethanol	• Does not affect the performance of the car. • Can save money. • Made from renewable resources. • Less carbon emissions. • Less carbon monoxide produced.	• Need to pay out to convert engine. • Much more sugar will need to be grown to meet demand. • Price of sugar is likely to rise due to increased demand. • When used as a fuel, alcohol can be a health risk. • Produces less energy than petrol when it burns.
Hydrogen	• Burning releases lots of energy. • No harmful gases produced, only water vapour which does not harm the environment.	• Expensive to produce from electricity. • Difficult to store safely.

11.4

How are polymers and ethanol made from oil?

Fractions produced from the distillation of crude oil can be cracked and used to make polymers, and ethene can be used to make ethanol. To understand this, you need to know…

- how hydrocarbons are cracked
- how fuels can be produced from cracking
- how ethanol is produced
- about the properties and uses of polymers.

Cracking Hydrocarbons

Longer-chain hydrocarbons can be **cracked** or broken down into shorter chains, which release energy more quickly by burning.

Hydrocarbons are cracked by heating them until they vaporise, then passing the vapour over a heated catalyst, where a thermal decomposition reaction takes place.

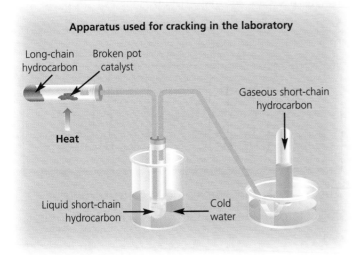

Apparatus used for cracking in the laboratory

Long-chain hydrocarbon
Broken pot catalyst
Gaseous short-chain hydrocarbon
Heat
Liquid short-chain hydrocarbon
Cold water

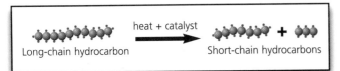

Long-chain hydrocarbon → heat + catalyst → Short-chain hydrocarbons

The products of cracking include alkanes and unsaturated hydrocarbons called **alkenes**. Some of the products are useful as fuels.

Making Alcohol from Ethene

Ethanol is an **alcohol**. It can be produced by reacting steam with ethene at a moderately high temperature and pressure in the presence of a catalyst, phosphoric acid.

Ethene + Steam —phosphoric acid→ Ethanol

Ethanol can be used as a…

- solvent
- fuel
- component in alcoholic drinks.

Alkenes (Unsaturated Hydrocarbons)

We have already seen that carbon atoms can form single bonds with other atoms; they can also form double bonds. Some of the products of cracking are hydrocarbon molecules with at least one double bond; this is an unsaturated hydrocarbon and it is known as an alkene.

The general formula for alkenes is C_nH_{2n}. The simplest alkene is ethene, C_2H_4, which is made up of 4 hydrogen atoms and 2 carbon atoms. As you can see in the diagram below, ethene contains one double carbon carbon bond.

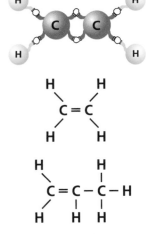

Here is another way of representing alkenes…
Ethene, C_2H_4

Propene, C_3H_6

Not all the carbon atoms are linked to 4 other atoms; a double carbon carbon bond is present instead. Because they are not 'fully occupied', i.e. they are unsaturated, they are useful for making other molecules, especially **polymers**.

Unit 1

Polymerisation

Because alkenes are unsaturated (have a double bond), they are very reactive. When small alkene molecules (monomers) join together to form long-chain molecules (polymers) without producing another substance, it is called **polymerisation**.

The properties of polymers depend on what they are made from and the conditions under which they are made. The materials commonly called plastics are all synthetic polymers. They are produced commercially on a very large scale and have a wide range of properties and uses. Polymers and plastics were first discovered in about 1933.

Making Poly(ethene) from Ethene

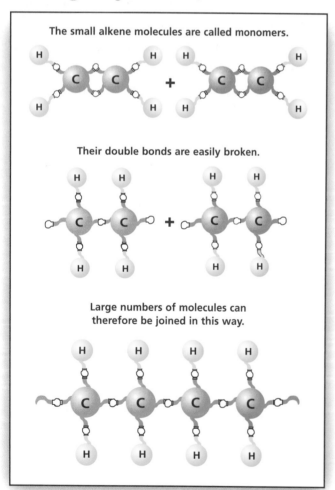

The resulting long-chain molecule is a polymer – in this case poly(ethene), often called polythene. Poly(propene) can be made in a similar way.

Representing Polymerisation

A more convenient form of representing polymerisation is…

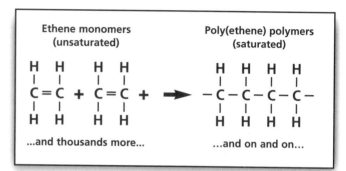

General Formula for Polymerisation

This formula can be used to represent the formation of any simple polymer:

$$n \left(\begin{array}{c} | \quad | \\ C = C \\ | \quad | \end{array} \right) \longrightarrow \left\{ \begin{array}{c} | \quad | \\ C - C \\ | \quad | \end{array} \right\}_n$$

where n is a very large number

For example, if we take 'n' molecules of propene we can produce poly(propene), which is used to make crates and ropes:

$$n \left(\begin{array}{cc} H & CH_3 \\ | & | \\ C &= C \\ | & | \\ H & H \end{array} \right) \xrightarrow[\text{catalyst}]{\text{pressure}} \left(\begin{array}{cc} H & CH_3 \\ | & | \\ C & - C \\ | & | \\ H & H \end{array} \right)_n$$

And 'n' molecules of chloroethene can produce polychloroethene (also known as polyvinyl chloride or PVC):

$$n \left(\begin{array}{cc} H & Cl \\ | & | \\ C &= C \\ | & | \\ H & H \end{array} \right) \xrightarrow[\text{catalyst}]{\text{pressure}} \left(\begin{array}{cc} H & Cl \\ | & | \\ C & - C \\ | & | \\ H & H \end{array} \right)_n$$

Polymers are classified by the reactions by which they are formed.

Polymers

Polymers have many useful applications and new uses are being developed.

Polymers and composites are widely used in medicine and dentistry:

- Implantable materials are used for hard and soft tissue surgery, replacing and fusing damaged bone and cartilage.
- Hard-wearing anti-bacterial dental cements, coatings and fillers have been produced.
- Hydrogels can be used as wound dressings.
- Silicone hydrogel contact lenses have been developed over the last few years. Research has shown that people who wear this type of contact lens have a 5% lower risk of developing severe eye infections.

Polymers and composites can be used to coat fabrics with a waterproof layer. Smart materials, including shape memory polymers, are also increasingly more common.

Specific polymers can have different uses, e.g.

Polyvinyl Chloride (PVC) can be used to make waterproof items and drain pipes and can also be used as an electrical insulator.

Polystyrene is used to make the casing for electrical appliances, and it can be expanded to make protective packaging.

Poly(ethene) is commonly used to make plastic bags and bottles.

Poly(propene) can be used to make crates and ropes.

Disposing of Plastics

Because plastic is such a versatile material and it is cheap and easy to produce we tend to generate a large amount of plastic waste.

There are various ways of disposing of plastics, unfortunately some of them have an impact on the environment.

1 Landfill Sites

The problem with most plastics is that they are non-biodegradable. Microorganisms have no effect on them, so they will not decompose and rot away. The use of landfill sites means that plastic waste builds up. However, research is being carried out on the development of biodegradable plastics.

2 Burning

Burning plastics produces air pollution. The production of carbon dioxide contributes to the Greenhouse Effect which results in global warming. Some plastics cannot be burned at all because they produce toxic fumes.

How Science Works

You need to be able to evaluate the social and economic advantages and disadvantages of using products from crude oil as fuels or as raw materials for plastic and other chemicals.

Crude oil is one of our most important natural resources. It is hard to imagine what our lives would be like without the products we can get from crude oil. Transport would come to a standstill, there would be no more plastics and detergents, and the pharmaceutical industry would not be able to get essential raw materials, so medicines would run out.

Crude oil can be used to make tough, lightweight, waterproof and breathable fabrics for clothes; paint for cars; dyes; packaging and communication equipment. However, it is important to weigh up the advantages of the products we can get from crude oil against the disadvantages of using it as a raw material.

Advantages of Crude Oil
• Refining crude oil provides jobs. • The fractions of crude oil have many uses. • Provides raw materials for industry. • Provides fuel for transport.
Disadvantages of Crude Oil
• Oil spills damage the environment. • Air pollution. • Increases global warming. • Produces non-biodegradable material.

You need to be able to consider and evaluate the social, economic and environmental impacts of the uses, disposal and recycling of polymers.

Plastics (polymers) are everywhere. There is a wide range of polymers with different, highly useful physical properties: some polymers are flexible, others are rigid; some have a low density, whereas others are very dense. They can be transparent or opaque. They are waterproof and resistant to corrosion and they can be used as a protective layer.

However, although polymers are relatively cheap to produce, the cost to society and the environment needs to be considered. Pollution, and its effects on residents who live near polymer-producing factories, is a major issue. And the disposal of polymers once they have been used needs to be addressed, as burning them produces harmful and sometimes toxic gases.

Advantages of Polymers
• Cheap to make. • Many uses because of their different properties. • Provide jobs in firms which make the polymer and the product. • Some polymers can be recycled, melted down and made into something else which saves valuable natural resources. • If polymers are used instead of wood, fewer trees will have to be cut down.
Disadvantages of Polymers
• People do not like to live near polymer-producing industrial works. • Some people think plastic products look cheap compared with natural materials. • Made from oil, a non-renewable resource. • Most plastics are not biodegradable so there is a problem of how to get rid of them. • Landfill sites are ugly. • Give off toxic fumes when they burn. • Sorting types of polymers for recycling can be expensive.

You need to be able to evaluate the advantages and disadvantages of making ethanol from renewable and non-renewable sources.

Using Non-renewable Sources

Ethanol can be produced by reacting steam with ethene at a moderately high temperature and pressure in the presence of the catalyst, phosphoric acid.

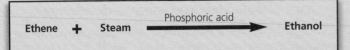

Ethene + Steam →(Phosphoric acid) Ethanol

Using Renewable Sources

Ethanol can also be produced by the fermentation of sugars. Water and yeast are mixed with the raw materials at just above room temperature. Enzymes, which are biological catalysts found in the yeast, react with the sugars to form ethanol and carbon dioxide. The carbon dioxide is allowed to escape from the reaction vessel, but air is prevented from entering it. The ethanol is separated from the reaction mixture by fractional distillation when the reaction is over.

Water + Yeast + Sugars → Ethanol + Carbon dioxide

One problem with the production of ethanol is that it can be oxidised by air (in certain conditions) to produce ethanoic acid. The presence of ethanoic acid results in alcoholic drinks turning sour.

Method	Advantages	Disadvantages
Reacting ethene with steam	• Fast rate of production. • High-quality ethanol produced. • Can be produced continuously. • Best method for making large quantities.	• Uses non-renewable sources.
Fermentation	• Renewable. • Can be produced in batches. • Fairly high-quality ethanol produced after fractional distillation. • Best method for making small quantities.	• Slow rate of production. • Ethanol not as good quality as that produced by reacting ethene with steam.

Unit 1

How can plant oils be used?

Oils can be extracted from plants and used for many purposes. To understand this, you need to know...
- how oils are extracted from plants
- the properties and uses of oils.

Getting Oil from Plants

Many plants produce fruit, seeds and nuts that are rich in **oils**, which can be extracted and changed into consumer products. Some common examples you might find in the food you eat are...
- sunflower oil
- olive oil
- oilseed rape
- palm kernel oil.

Oil can be extracted from plant materials by pressing (crushing) them or by distillation. This removes the water and other impurities from the plant material.

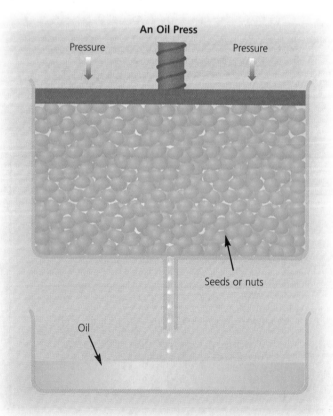

An Oil Press

Pressure   Pressure

Seeds or nuts

Oil

Vegetable Oils

Vegetable oils are important **foods** and **fuels** as they provide nutrients and a lot of energy. Some vehicles can now be converted to use vegetable oils as their fuel instead of petrol or diesel.

Vegetable oils contain double carbon carbon bonds, so they are described as **unsaturated**. They can be detected using bromine water. They react with the orange-coloured bromine water to decolourise it. The bromine becomes part of the compound, by breaking the double bond. For example...

$$\begin{array}{c} H \quad H \\ | \quad\; | \\ C = C \\ | \quad\; | \\ H \quad H \end{array} \; + \; Br_2 \; \longrightarrow \; \begin{array}{c} H \quad H \\ | \quad\; | \\ H - C - C - H \\ | \quad\; | \\ Br \;\; Br \end{array}$$

Ethene (double bond compound)	+	Bromine water	→	Dibromoethene (single bond compound)

Oils do not dissolve in water as the liquids have different densities. A mixture of oil and water is called an **emulsion**. If oil and water are mixed thoroughly, droplets of oil can be seen dispersed in the water.

Emulsions are thicker than oil or water and have a better texture, appearance and coating ability. They have many uses, e.g. salad dressing and ice cream.

If you mix some olive oil and vinegar together you can make a salad dressing. However, it does not stay mixed for very long as the water particles in the vinegar clump together and the oil particles clump together. The mixture can be seen to separate into two layers. You can make the salad dressing last longer by adding some mustard to it before shaking the mixture up. This stops the separate layers forming. The mustard is an emulsifying agent. Many different emulsifying agents are used in the manufacture of food to stop vegetable oils and water forming separate layers.

The Manufacture of Margarine

As a general guide, the more double carbon carbon bonds present in a substance, the lower its melting point. This means that unsaturated fats, e.g. vegetable oils, tend to have melting points below room temperature and are called oils.

For some purposes you might need a solid fat, for example, to spread on your bread or to use to make cakes and pastries. You can raise the melting point of an oil to above room temperature by removing some or all of the double carbon carbon bonds.

When ethene and hydrogen are heated together in the presence of a nickel catalyst, a reaction takes place which removes the double carbon carbon bonds to produce ethane. This process is called **hydrogenation**.

$$\begin{array}{ccccc}
\overset{\displaystyle H}{\underset{\displaystyle H}{\overset{|}{\underset{|}{C}}}} = \overset{\displaystyle H}{\underset{\displaystyle H}{\overset{|}{\underset{|}{C}}}} & + & H_2 & \xrightarrow[\text{catalyst}]{\text{nickel}} & H - \overset{\displaystyle H}{\underset{\displaystyle H}{\overset{|}{\underset{|}{C}}}} - \overset{\displaystyle H}{\underset{\displaystyle H}{\overset{|}{\underset{|}{C}}}} - H
\end{array}$$

Unsaturated fat **+** Hydrogen ⟶ Saturated fat

Margarine is manufactured from unsaturated vegetable oils like sunflower oil. The oil is reacted with hydrogen, at a temperature of around 60°C in the presence of a nickel catalyst and some of the double bonds are hydrogenated. Removing more double bonds makes the margarine harder.

Additives

Many processed foods have different substances added to them to improve their look, texture or flavour or to help preserve them. Some of these additives are natural, but the majority are produced by the chemical industry.

Additives have to be shown in the list of ingredients on the label. Some of the additives that are allowed to be added to foods are called E-numbers.

Chemical Analysis

Chemical analysis can be used to identify additives in food. **Chromatography** is a method used to identify artificial colours.

Chromatography identifies unknown substances, by comparing them to known substances. A sample of four known substances (A, B, C and D) and the unknown substance (X) are put on a 'start line' on a piece of paper, which is then dipped into a solvent. As the solvent is absorbed by the paper, it dissolves the samples and carries them up the paper. The substances will move up the paper by differing amounts due to different substances having different solubilities. Substance X can be identified by comparing the horizontal spots.

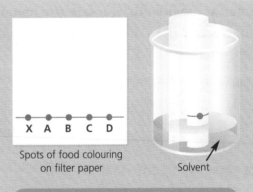

Apparatus for chromatography

Spots of food colouring on filter paper

Solvent

By comparing food colourings A, B, C and D to substance X, we can see that substance X is food colouring D.

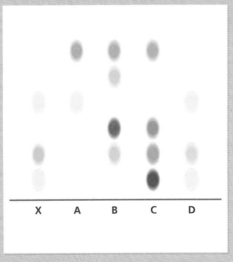

A chromatogram showing how the food colourings have split into their dyes

How Science Works

You need to be able to evaluate the effects of using vegetable oils in food and the impacts on diet and health.

Oils have many uses. However, the amount of saturated fats we consume needs to be carefully controlled to reduce the risk of heart disease.

Vegetable oil is a healthy alternative to using fats derived from animals because it contains monounsaturated fats which can lower blood cholesterol levels, and it contains no cholesterol.

However, it is important to remember that you should not consume too much of any oil because this would not lead to a healthy balanced diet. Where possible, unsaturated fats such as olive oil should be used to reduce the health risks. However, using other oils occasionally would not be too bad for your health.

You need to be able to evaluate the benefits, drawbacks and risks of using vegetable oil to produce fuels.

Cars can now be converted so that they can run on vegetable oil, instead of petrol or diesel. Although in many ways this is a more environmentally friendly option, it has not yet become widespread, and only a few cars have been converted.

Advantages	Disadvantages
<ul><li>Cheaper than diesel or petrol.</li><li>Fewer pollutant gases produced – virtually carbon neutral.</li><li>No change to performance of car.</li><li>Renewable source.</li></ul>	<ul><li>High cost of conversion kit.</li><li>Need to inform Customs and Excise.</li><li>Unpleasant smell.</li><li>Inconvenience of filling up your car – vegetable oil currently not an option at petrol stations.</li><li>Increased demand may put up prices for food made using vegetable oil.</li></ul>

You need to be able to evaluate the uses, benefits, drawbacks and risks of ingredients and additives in foods.

Food additives are substances that are put into foods for various reasons. Some types of additives that are used in foods are...

- colourings (e.g. curcumin, E100) – to replace natural colouring of the food that can be lost during cooking
- flavourings (e.g. monosodium glutamate, E621) – to enhance and replace flavours that can be lost during processing
- emulsifiers and stabilisers (e.g. lecithin, E322) – to mix ingredients that would normally separate to give a consistent texture
- antioxidants (e.g. ascorbic acid or vitamin C, E300) – to help stop substances from combining with oxygen in the air, which would make the food 'go off'
- preservatives (e.g. sulfur dioxide, E220) – to prevent food from rotting due to bacteria and moulds
- sweeteners (e.g. sorbitol, E420) make food sweeter.

Although additives can be very useful, we need to carefully weigh up the benefits of using them against the risks involved.

Advantages	Disadvantages
<ul><li>Can increase the appeal of food.</li><li>Can extend the shelf-life of food.</li><li>Can reduce the energy in food (good for slimming products).</li><li>Can be better for teeth (e.g. sweetener).</li></ul>	<ul><li>Introduces substances that are not needed by the body.</li><li>Can cause headaches, allergies and asthma attacks.</li><li>Can adversely affect behaviour, particularly in children, e.g. hyperactivity.</li><li>Some are considered to be harmful. (They have been banned in some countries.)</li></ul>

11.6

What are the changes in the Earth and its atmosphere?

The Earth is protected by the atmosphere, which has remained fairly constant for the last 200 million years but is now changing. To understand this, you need to know…

- about the structure of the Earth
- about tectonic activity
- what the atmosphere consists of.

Structure of the Earth

The Earth is nearly spherical and has a layered structure that consists of…

- a thin crust – thickness varies between 10km and 100km
- a mantle – extends almost halfway to the centre and has all the properties of a solid even though it does flow very slowly
- a core (made of nickel and iron) – over half of the Earth's radius with a liquid outer part and a solid inner part.

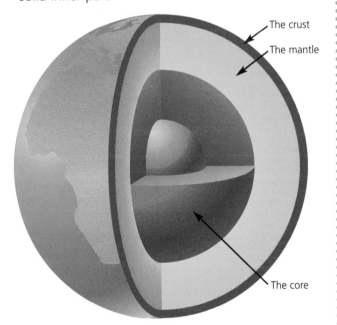

The crust
The mantle
The core

The average density of the Earth is much greater than the average density of the rocks which form the crust, because the interior is made of a different, denser material than that of the crust.

Although there does not seem to be much going on, the Earth and its crust are very dynamic. Rocks at the Earth's surface are continually being broken up, reformed and changed in an ongoing cycle of events, known as the rock cycle. It is just that the changes take place over a very long time.

Tectonic Theory

At one time people used to believe that features on the Earth's surface were caused by shrinkage when the Earth cooled, following its formation. However, as scientists have found out more about the Earth, this theory has now been rejected.

A long time ago, scientists noticed that the east coast of South America and the west coast of Africa have…

- similar patterns of rocks, which contain fossils of the same plants and animals, e.g. the Mesosaurus

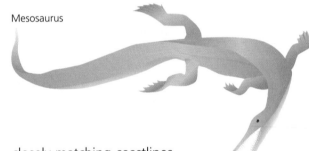

Mesosaurus

- closely matching coastlines.

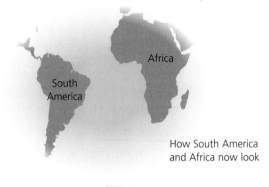

Africa
South America

How South America and Africa now look

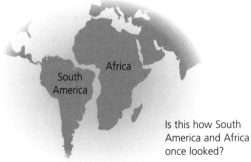

Africa
South America

Is this how South America and Africa once looked?

Tectonic Theory (continued)

This evidence led Alfred Wegener to propose that, even though they are now separated by thousands of kilometres of ocean, South America and Africa had at one time been part of a single land mass.

How it once was

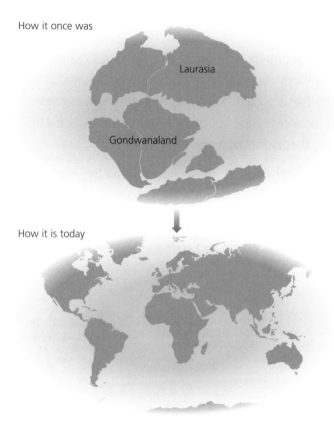

He proposed that the movement of the crust was responsible for the separation of the land (or continental drift), which explains the movement of the continents from how they were (as Gondwanaland and Laurasia) to how they look today. This is known as **tectonic theory**. Unfortunately, Wegener was unable to explain *how* the crust moved and it took more than 50 years for scientists to discover this.

We now know that the Earth's lithosphere (the crust and the upper part of the mantle) is 'cracked' into several large pieces called **tectonic plates**. Intense heat, released by radioactive decay deep in the Earth, causes hot molten rock to rise to the surface at the boundary between the plates, causing the tectonic plates to move apart very slowly, at speeds of a few centimetres per year.

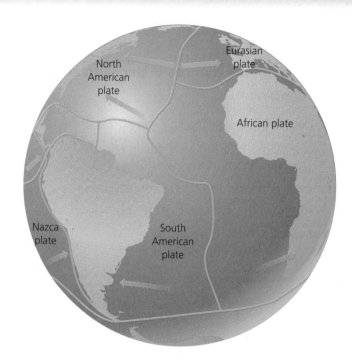

In convection in a gas or a liquid, the matter rises as it is heated, then as it gets further away from the heat source it cools and sinks down again. The same happens in the Earth. The hot molten rock rises to the surface, creating new crust. The older crust, which is cooler, then sinks down where the convection current starts to fall. This causes the land masses on these plates to move slowly across the globe.

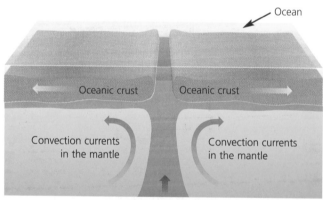

Although the movements are usually small and gradual, they can sometimes be sudden and disastrous. Earthquakes and volcanic eruptions are common occurrences at plate boundaries. As yet, scientists cannot predict *when* these events will occur, due to the difficulty in taking appropriate measurements, but at least they do know *where* these events are likely to occur.

Tectonic Plate Movement

The movement of the tectonic plates can happen suddenly due to a build up in pressure, and can sometimes have disastrous consequences, e.g. earthquakes and tsunamis. Tectonic plates can move in three ways:

1 Slide Past Each Other

When plates slide, huge stresses and strains build up in the crust which eventually have to be released in order for movement to occur. This 'release' of energy results in an earthquake. A classic example of this is the West Coast of North America (especially California).

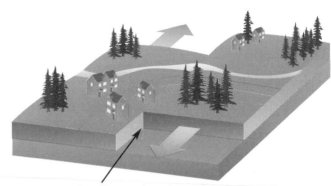

An earthquake will occur along the line where the two plates meet

2 Move Away from Each Other – Constructive Plate Boundaries

When plates move away from each other at an oceanic ridge, fractures occur. Molten rock rises to the surface, where it solidifies to form new ocean floor. This is known as sea floor spreading. Because new rock is being formed, these are called **constructive** plate boundaries.

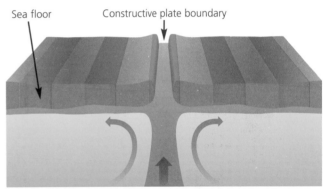

Sea floor   Constructive plate boundary

Magma rising

3 Move Towards Each Other – Destructive Plate Boundaries

As plates are moving away from each other in some places it follows that they must be moving towards each other in other places. When plates collide, one is forced under the other, so these are called **destructive** plate boundaries. Earthquakes and volcanoes are common on destructive plate boundaries.

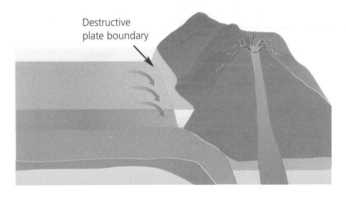

Destructive plate boundary

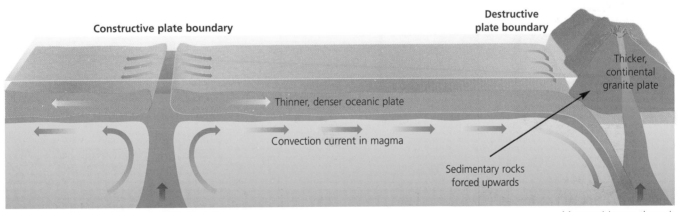

Constructive plate boundary

Destructive plate boundary

Thicker, continental granite plate

Thinner, denser oceanic plate

Convection current in magma

Sedimentary rocks forced upwards

Magma rising and solidifying to form new ocean floor (few centimetres per year)

Magma rising up through continental crust

Unit 1

The Earth's Atmosphere

Since the formation of the earth 4.6 billion years ago the atmosphere has changed a lot. The timescale, however, is enormous because one billion years is one thousand million (1 000 000 000) years!

Time Scale	Composition of the Atmosphere	Key Factors and Events which Shaped the Atmosphere
Formation of the Earth 4 billion years ago 3.5 3 billion years ago 2.5 2 billion years ago 1.5 1 billion years ago 0.5 now	Other gases CO_2 Decrease in carbon dioxide and other gases Increase in oxygen and nitrogen Other gases CO_2 O_2 N_2 Carbon dioxide much reduced Increase in oxygen and nitrogen Other gases CO_2 N_2 O_2	Intense volcanic activity releases… • mainly carbon dioxide (like the atmospheres of Mars and Venus today) • small amounts of other gases • water vapour which condenses to form the oceans. Green plants evolve and… • carbon dioxide is reduced as the plants take it in and give out oxygen • microorganisms that cannot tolerate oxygen are killed off • carbon from carbon dioxide in the air becomes locked up in sedimentary rocks as carbonates and fossil fuels • other gases react with the oxygen now available to release nitrogen, which is also produced by bacteria removing nitrates from decaying plant material. • The oxygen and nitrogen in the atmosphere are now much increased. • Carbon dioxide has decreased significantly.

Composition of the Atmosphere

Our atmosphere has been more or less the same for about 200 million years. The pie chart (below) shows how it is made up. Water vapour may also be present in varying quantities (0–3%).

The noble gases (in Group 0 of the periodic table) are all chemically unreactive gases and are used in filament layers and electric discharge tubes. Helium is much less dense than air and is used in balloons.

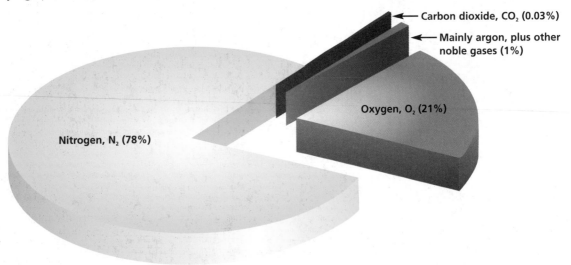

Carbon dioxide, CO_2 (0.03%)

Mainly argon, plus other noble gases (1%)

Oxygen, O_2 (21%)

Nitrogen, N_2 (78%)

Changes to the Atmosphere

The level of carbon dioxide in the atmosphere today is increasing due to…

- volcanic activity – geological activity moves carbonate rocks deep into the earth. During volcanic activity they may release carbon dioxide back into the atmosphere.
- burning of fossil fuels – burning carbon, which has been locked up in fossil fuels for millions of years, releases carbon dioxide into the atmosphere.

The level of carbon dioxide in the atmosphere is reduced by the reaction between carbon dioxide and sea water. Increased carbon dioxide in the atmosphere increases the reaction between carbon dioxide and sea water. This reaction produces insoluble carbonates (mainly calcium) which are deposited as sediment, and soluble hydrogen carbonates (mainly calcium and magnesium). These form the sedimentary rocks in the Earth's crust.

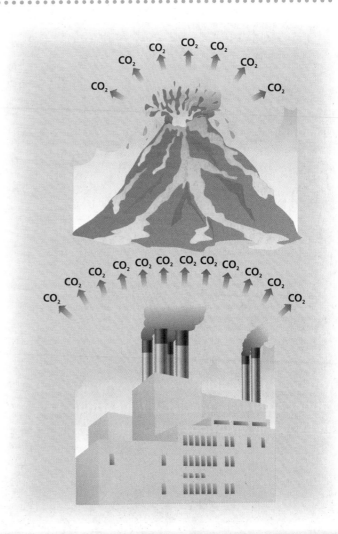

How Science Works

You need to be able to explain why the theory of crustal movement (continental drift) was not generally accepted for many years after it was proposed.

About 200 years ago, most geologists thought that the Earth had gone through a period of being extremely hot and so consequently had dried out and contracted, or shrunk, as it cooled. Features of the Earth, such as mountain ranges, were thought to have been wrinkles that formed in the Earth's crust as it shrank.

At this point, insufficient data had been collected to show that the continents were in fact moving, and nobody produced any evidence to contradict the theory of the Earth shrinking until the early 1900s.

Then Alfred Wegener studied certain features of the Earth (see p.33–34), which prompted him to propose his theory of continental drift in 1915. This theory proposed that the Earth is made up of plates which have moved slowly apart. Most geologists at the time said that this theory was impossible, although a few did support Wegener.

In the 1950s scientists were able to investigate the ocean floor and found new evidence to support Wegener's theory. They discovered that although he was wrong about some aspects, the basis for his theory was correct.

By the 1960s, geologists were convinced by the theory of continental drift and can now use it to explain many geological features and occurrences caused by moving tectonic plates. Evidence now shows that the sea floor is spreading outwards and convection currents in the mantle cause movement of the crust.

You need to be able to explain why scientists cannot accurately predict when earthquakes and volcanic eruptions will occur.

To understand how earthquakes and volcanic eruptions occur, we need to consider the movement of the tectonic plates. They can stay in the same position for some time, resisting a build up of strain, and then when the strain becomes too great they can suddenly move.

However, it is impossible to predict exactly when this will happen because the plates do not move in regular patterns. Scientists can measure the strain in underground rocks to see if they can calculate when an earthquake is likely to happen, but they are unlikely to be able to give an exact forecast.

A volcano erupts when molten rock rises up into the spaces between the rocks near the surface. Scientists have instruments which can identify these changes, and therefore warn of imminent eruptions. However, sometimes the molten rock cools, so the magma does not reach the surface and the volcano does not erupt. So, other factors which are hard to predict can affect whether a volcano erupts or not.

Therefore, despite having very sophisticated equipment which monitors volcano activity and areas prone to earthquakes, scientists cannot always predict exactly when they might happen.

How Science Works

You need to be able to explain and evaluate the effects of human activities on the atmosphere.

Most human activities, especially those used to create heat and energy, can produce pollutants which are harmful to the atmosphere. Some of these activities and their impact on the atmosphere are listed below:

The burning of fossil fuels creates the gases sulfur dioxide and carbon dioxide. Sulfur dioxide contributes to the formation of acid rain which can erode buildings and add acid to lakes and the soil.

The carbon dioxide content of the air used to be roughly constant (0.03%) but it has been increased by the growth in population, which raises energy requirements.

Deforestation means less photosynthesis takes place. An increase in the level of carbon dioxide is believed to be responsible for global warming and climate change.

The combustion of petrol and diesel involves the reaction of nitrogen and oxygen at very high temperatures in car engines to provide oxides of nitrogen which are pollutants. Carbon monoxide is produced by the incomplete combustion of fuels. It is a poisonous gas which eventually oxidises into carbon dioxide, which leads to global warming.

So, what can we do to reduce the pollutants? Humans need to create energy to heat homes, power their cars, etc. but we need to look at the effect various fuels have on the environment and consider alternative methods of producing energy in order to limit the impact we have on the planet.

- Cars fitted with catalytic converters reduce the levels of carbon monoxide and oxides of nitrogen.
- Alternative forms of energy can reduce pollutants, e.g. wind farms and hydroelectricity.
- Power stations can use fuels which reduce atmospheric pollution.

The European Union and the United Kingdom have made laws to scontrol the pollution levels. These laws need to be regulated and monitored, and every country needs to control their pollution levels.

Example Questions

For Unit 1, you will either have to complete two objective tests (matching and multiple choice questions) or one written paper (longer, structured questions).

1   The elements in the periodic table are arranged in groups.

Which of these statements best describes a periodic group?

A A group contains elements with similar properties. .... ☑

B A group contains elements in alphabetical order. .... ☐

C A group contains a random selection of elements. .... ☐

D A group contains elements that react with each other. .... ☐   *(1 mark)*   ①

2   Crude oil is made up of hydrocarbons. What is a hydrocarbon?

A A mixture of lots of different elements. .... ☐

B A molecule made up of only carbon and hydrogen atoms. .... ☑

C A compound of carbon and water. .... ☐

D One of the elements in the periodic table. .... ☐   *(1 mark)*   ①

3   The boiling points of eight hydrocarbons are displayed in the following table:

No. of carbon atoms in the hydrocarbon	1	2	3	4	5	6	7	8
Boiling point °C	-150	-98	-45	2	32	66	98	120

(a) Suggest a hypothesis that could have been investigated when the data in the table was collected.

    The number of carbon atoms in a hydrocarbon will affect its boiling point.

    (1 mark)

(b) What is the independent variable?

    The number of carbon atoms in the hydrocarbon.

    (1 mark)

(c) What is the dependent variable?

    The boiling point.

    (1 mark)

(d) If you drew a line graph of these results which variable would you put on the horizontal axis?

    The independent variable (number of carbon atoms in hydrocarbon).

    (1 mark)

(e) Describe the relationship between the two variables in the results table.

    A positive correlation: as the number of carbon atoms increases, the boiling point of the hydrocarbon increases.

    (1 mark)

(f) Name one key variable you should control in order to make this investigation a fair test.

    Amount (volume) of hydrocarbon tested.

    (1 mark)

(g) Suggest one change you could make to your method in order to improve the accuracy of these results.

    Measure each of the boiling points more than once and find the mean.

    (1 mark)   ⑦

① If you are unsure about the answer to a multiple-choice question, eliminate the options that you know are wrong first.

② Read the question and all the options carefully. For this one, the clue is in the name!

③ A hypothesis suggests the relationship between two variables. It is always a statement (never a question)!

④ The independent variable is the one being controlled.

⑤ The dependent variable is measured each time the independent variable is changed, to see if there is a relationship between the two.

⑥ The independent variable always goes on the horizontal axis (or x-axis).

⑦ Only comment on what the data tells you – nothing else!

⑧ In a fair test, only the independent variable can affect the dependent variable. All outside variables are kept the same.

⑨ Repeating measurements helps identify errors, and finding the mean (average) gives a best estimate of the true value.

Alkane – a saturated hydrocarbon

Alkene – an unsaturated hydrocarbon (with at least one double carbon carbon bond)

Alloy – a mixture of two or more metals or a mixture of one metal and a non-metal

Atom – the smallest part of an element which can enter into chemical reactions

Catalyst – a substance that increases the rate of a chemical reaction, whilst remaining chemically unchanged itself

Chemical formula – a way of showing the elements present in a substance

Chemical reaction – a process in which one or more substances are changed into others

Compound – a substance consisting of two or more elements chemically combined together

Decompose – to break down

Element – a substance that consists of only one type of atom

Emulsion – a mixture of oil and water

Fossil fuels – fuels formed in the ground, over millions of years, from the remains of dead plants and animals

Fuel – a substance that releases heat or energy when combined with oxygen

Hydrocarbon – a compound containing only hydrogen and carbon

Hydrogenation – the process in which hydrogen is used to harden vegetable oils

Molecule – the simplest structural unit of an element or compound

Non-biodegradable – a substance that does not decompose naturally

Ore – a naturally occurring mineral from which a metal can be extracted

Polymer – a giant long-chained hydrocarbon

Sedimentary rocks – rocks formed by the accumulation of sediment

Smart alloy – an alloy which can change shape and then return to its original shape

Tectonic plates – huge sections of the Earth's crust which move relative to one another

12.1 and 12.2

How do subatomic particles help us to understand the structure of substances?

The arrangement of electrons in an atom can be used to explain what happens when elements react. To understand this, you need to know…

- about protons, neutrons and electrons
- about shells / energy levels in atoms
- the difference between a compound and a mixture
- about the structures that compounds can make.

How do structures influence the properties and uses of substances?

Substances can be held together by different structures, which have different properties. The forces between bonds are strong; the forces between molecules are weaker. Nanomaterials are very small materials with new properties. To understand this, you need to know…

- that substances can be solids, liquids or gases
- the structures of compounds
- how substances can conduct electricity
- about the developments in nanoscience.

Subatomic Particles

The diagram below shows the subatomic particles in an atom of helium.

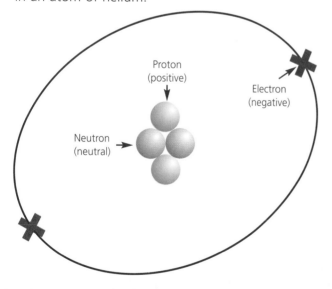

Atoms have a small central nucleus which is made up of protons and neutrons. The nucleus is surrounded by electrons. Protons, neutrons and electrons have relative electrical charges.

Atomic Particle		Relative Charge
Proton		+1
Neutron		0
Electron		-1

All atoms of a particular element have an equal number of protons and electrons, which means that atoms have no overall charge.

All atoms of a particular element have the same number of protons. Atoms of different elements have different numbers of protons. This is known as their **atomic number**. Elements are arranged in the modern periodic table in order of the number of their atoms.

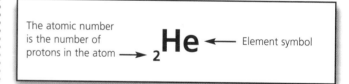

The atomic number is the number of protons in the atom → $_2$He ← Element symbol

Electron configuration tells us how the electrons are arranged around the nucleus in energy levels or shells.

The electrons in an atom occupy the lowest available energy levels (i.e. the innermost available shells).

- The first level or shell can only contain a maximum of 2 electrons.
- The energy levels or shells after this can hold a maximum of 8 electrons.

We write the electron configuration as a series of numbers, e.g. oxygen is 2, 6 and aluminium is 2, 8, 3.

Electronic Structure

The periodic table arranges the elements in terms of their electronic structure. Elements in the same group have the same number of electrons in their outermost shell (this number also coincides with the group number). Elements in the same group therefore have similar properties. From left to right, across each period, a particular energy level is gradually filled with electrons. In the next period, the next energy level is filled, etc.

The Alkali Metals (Group 1)

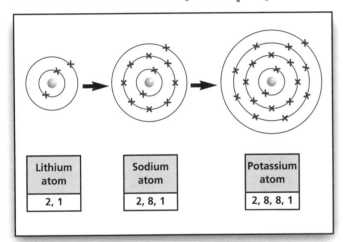

They all have similar properties, because they have the same number of electrons (one) in their outermost shell, i.e. the highest occupied energy level contains one electron. They react with non-metal elements to form ionic compounds (see p.44), where the metal ion has a single positive charge.

The Halogens (Group 7)

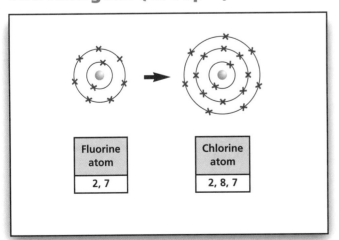

They all have similar properties, because they have the same number of electrons (7) in their outermost shell, i.e. the highest occupied energy level contains 7 electrons.

They react with alkali metals to form ionic compounds (see p.44), where the halide ions have a single negative charge.

Mixtures and Compounds

A **mixture** consists of two or more elements or compounds that are not chemically combined. The properties of the substances remain unchanged and specific to that substance.

Compounds are substances in which the atoms of two or more elements are chemically combined (not just mixed together).

Atoms can form chemical bonds by...
- sharing electrons (covalent bonds)
- gaining or losing electrons (ionic bonds).

Either way, when atoms form chemical bonds the arrangement of the outermost shell of electrons changes resulting in each atom getting a complete outer shell of electrons.

For most atoms this is eight electrons but for helium it is only two.

Simple Molecular Compounds

Gases, liquids and solids that have relatively low melting and boiling points consist of simple molecules. Because the molecules have no overall electric charge, they do not conduct electricity.

HT Substances that consist of simple molecules have weak forces of attraction between their molecules (inter-molecular), unlike the very strong bond that exists between two atoms. This is why they have low melting and boiling points.

Unit 2

The Ionic Bond

This occurs between a metal and a non-metal atom and involves a **transfer** of electrons from one atom to the other to form electrically charged **ions**, each of which has a complete outermost energy level or shell. This means that ions have the electronic structure of a noble gas. Atoms which **lose electrons** become **positively charged** ions while atoms which **gain electrons** become **negatively charged** ions.

Ionic compounds are giant structures of ions held together by strong forces of attraction between oppositely charged ions that act in all directions. This is called **ionic bonding**. Ionic compounds have high melting and boiling points.

Example 1 – Sodium and chlorine bond ionically to form sodium chloride, NaCl. The sodium (Na) atom has 1 electron in its outer shell which is transferred to the chlorine (Cl) atom so they both have 8 electrons in their outer shells. The atoms become ions Na^+ and Cl^- and the compound formed is sodium chloride, NaCl.

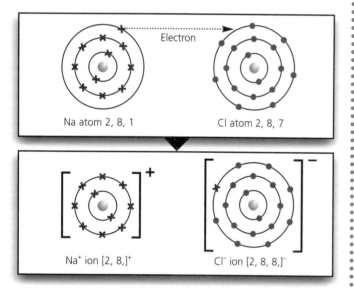

Na atom 2, 8, 1   Cl atom 2, 8, 7

Na^+ ion [2, 8,]$^+$ Cl^- ion [2, 8, 8,]$^-$

Example 2 – Calcium and chlorine bond ionically to form calcium chloride, $CaCl_2$. The calcium (Ca) atom has 2 electrons in its outer shell and a chlorine (Cl) atom only wants 1 electron therefore 2 Cl atoms are needed to give all 3 atoms 8 electrons in their outer shell. The atoms become ions Ca^{2+}, Cl^- and Cl^- and the compound formed is calcium chloride, $CaCl_2$.

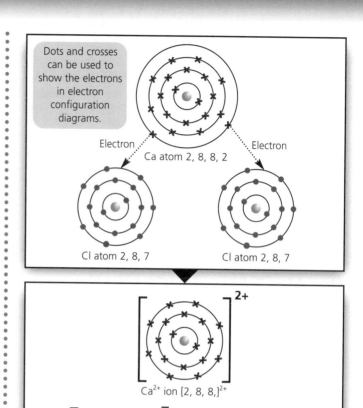

Dots and crosses can be used to show the electrons in electron configuration diagrams.

Electron   Ca atom 2, 8, 8, 2   Electron

Cl atom 2, 8, 7   Cl atom 2, 8, 7

Ca^{2+} ion [2, 8, 8,]$^{2+}$

Cl^- ion [2, 8, 8,]$^-$ Cl^- ion [2, 8, 8,]$^-$

Example 3 – Magnesium and oxygen bond ionically to form magnesium oxide, MgO. The magnesium (Mg) atom has 2 electrons in its outer shell which are transferred to the oxygen (O) atom so they both have 8 electrons in their outer shell. The atoms become ions Mg^{2+} and O^{2-} and the compound formed is magnesium oxide, MgO.

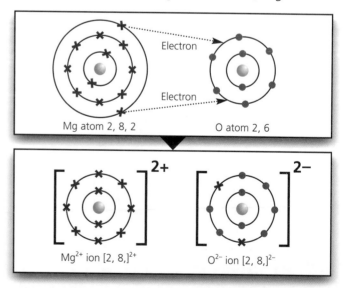

Electron

Electron

Mg atom 2, 8, 2   O atom 2, 6

Mg^{2+} ion [2, 8,]$^{2+}$ O^{2-} ion [2, 8,]$^{2-}$

The Covalent Bond

The **covalent bond** is a very strong bond which is formed when electrons are **shared**. This occurs between non-metal atoms.

Some covalently bonded substances have simple bonds (like H_2, Cl_2, O_2, HCl, H_2O, CH_4) whereas others have giant covalent structures, called macromolecules (e.g. diamond, silicon dioxide).

A chlorine atom has 7 electrons in its outermost shell. In order to bond with itself, an electron from each atom is shared to give both chlorine atoms 8 electrons in their outermost shell. This means each atom has a complete outer shell.

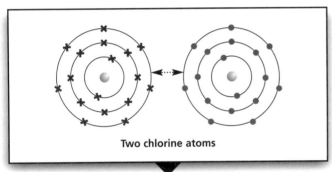

Two chlorine atoms

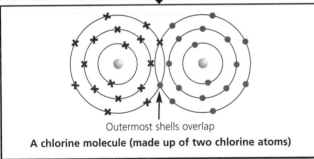

Outermost shells overlap

A chlorine molecule (made up of two chlorine atoms)

Atoms which share electrons often form molecules in which there are strong covalent bonds between the atoms in each molecule but not between molecules. This means that they usually have low melting and boiling points.

Chlorine molecules

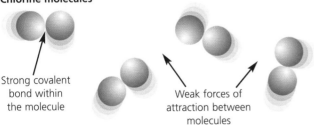

Strong covalent bond within the molecule

Weak forces of attraction between molecules

Covalent Bonding

You need to be familiar with the following examples, and know how to use three different methods for representing the covalent bonds in each molecule. Two forms are given in the examples below:

Water, H_2O		H—O—H (bent)
Chlorine, Cl_2		Cl — Cl
Hydrogen, H_2		H — H
Hydrogen chloride, HCl		H — Cl
Methane, CH_4		H—C—H with H above and below
Oxygen, O_2		O = O (a double bond)

The third form of representing covalent bonds is shown here for an ammonia molecule (NH_3). This is perhaps the most confusing method, and unless specifically asked for, you should use the other two methods.

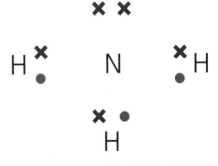

Unit 2

Giant Covalent Structures

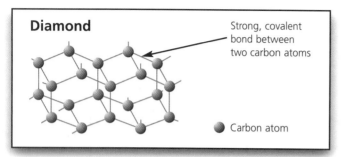

Diamond

Strong, covalent bond between two carbon atoms

• Carbon atom

Diamond is a form of carbon that has a giant, rigid covalent structure (lattice) where each carbon atom forms four covalent bonds with other carbon atoms.

The large number of covalent bonds results in diamond having a very high melting point which makes the diamond very hard.

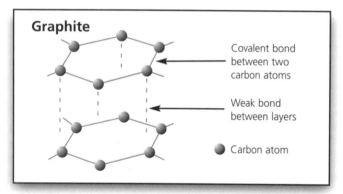

Graphite

Covalent bond between two carbon atoms

Weak bond between layers

• Carbon atom

Graphite is a form of carbon that has a giant covalent structure (lattice) in which each carbon atom forms three covalent bonds with other carbon atoms in a layered structure. The layers can slide past each other, making it soft and slippery.

HT Covalent bonds are very strong. There are weak forces of attraction between layers. In graphite, one electron from each carbon atom can be delocalised, which allows it to conduct heat and electricity.

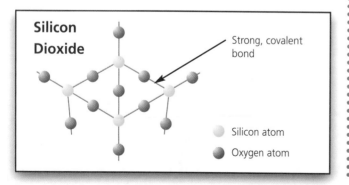

Silicon Dioxide

Strong, covalent bond

○ Silicon atom

● Oxygen atom

Silicon dioxide (SiO_2, also known as silica) has a giant, rigid covalent structure (lattice) similar to diamond, where each oxygen atom is joined to two silicon atoms and each silicon atom is joined to four oxygen atoms.

The large number of covalent bonds results in silicon dioxide having a very high melting point.

Giant Ionic Structures

+ Positively charged ions
− Negatively charged ions

A giant ionic structure is a regular structure (giant ionic lattice) held together by the strong forces of attraction (electrostatic forces) between oppositely charged ions. These forces act in all directions in the lattice. This results in them having high melting and boiling points.

Ionic compounds also conduct electricity when molten or in solution because the charged ions are free to move about and carry the current.

HT ## Metals

Metals have a giant structure in which electrons in the highest energy level can be delocalised.

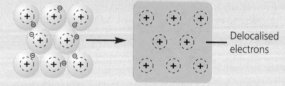

Delocalised electrons

This effectively produces a regular arrangement (lattice) of positive ions that are held together by electrons using electrostatic attraction.

These delocalised electrons…
• hold the atoms together in a regular structure
• allow the atoms to slide over each other so metals can be bent and shaped
• can move around freely, which allows the metal to conduct heat and electricity.

Nanoparticles and Nanostructures

Nanoscience is the study of structures that are 1–100 nanometres in size, roughly in the order of a few hundred atoms. One nanometre is 0.000 000 001m (one billionth of a metre) and is written as 1nm or 1m x 10^{-9}. (A human hair is around 20 000nm in diameter and a microorganism is around 200nm in diameter.)

Nanoparticles are tiny, tiny particles that can combine to form structures called **nanostructures**.

Nanostructures have always existed in naturally occurring substances such as liposomes. However, technology to enable them to be seen did not exist until the early 1980s. Scientists working with new technology (the scanning tunnelling microscope) were able to construct enlarged images of surfaces, allowing them to see atoms and molecules for the first time. By the early 1990s, atoms could be isolated and moved. This means nanostructures can be manipulated so materials can be developed that have new and specific properties, and can be used in industry.

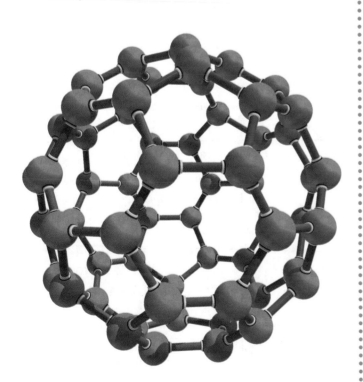

Fullerene-related carbon nanostructure

The properties of nanoparticles are different to the properties of the same materials in bulk. For example…

- electrons can move through an insulating layer of atoms
- nanoparticles are more sensitive to light, heat and magnetism
- nanoparticles possess a high surface area in relation to their volume.

A magnified representation of iron atoms in a ring around some surface state electrons

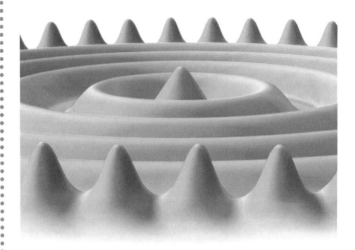

Nanocomposites

Other materials can be added to plastics to make stronger, stiffer and lighter materials, called **nanocomposite** materials. The characteristics of nanocomposites can be seen by looking at the nanostructures formed by the nanoparticles.

Nanocomposites are already being used in the car industry and others are being developed with medical and dental applications in mind. They are also used in energy storage and separation processing, highly selective sensors, new coatings, sunscreens, drug delivery systems, stronger and lighter construction materials, textile fibres and product-specific catalysts.

Smart materials are a type of nanostructure that can be designed so they have specific properties on a nanoscopic scale or behave in a certain way when subjected to certain conditions.

How Science Works

You need to be able to relate the properties of substances to their uses. Suggest the type of structure of a substance when you are given its properties.

*Higher Tier only.

Substance	Properties	Example – Uses	Structure
Metal	• Strong. • Shiny. • Malleable (bendy). • Good conductor of heat and electricity.*	• Steel – construction. • Gold – jewellery. • Aluminium, copper – pans, wires. • Copper – pipes, wires.	• The layers of atoms can slide over each other. • Giant structure of atoms held together with metallic bonds allowing outer electrons of each atom to move freely.*
Non-metal	• Brittle. • Insulator.	• Glass – bottles. • Wood – pan handles.	• Covalent bonds, no ions involved.
Polymer	• Lightweight. • Flexible. • Waterproof.	• Polyethene – plastic bags. • Shaped containers. • Polyvinyl chloride – rainwear.	• Long-chain structure of covalent bonded atoms. Forces between them are weak.
Ionic compound	• Hard, crystalline, soluble in water. • High melting points. • Insulator when solid but conducts electricity when molten or dissolved.	• Sodium chloride – food additive. • Sodium chloride – electrolysis.	• Force of attraction between oppositely charged ions formed by electronic transfer. A lattice results which is difficult to break down. In the solid state the ions are held in place. Once melted or dissolved they are free to move.
Molecular covalent	• Soft. • Low melting points. • Insulator.	• Gases. • Ammonia, nitrogen and oxygen gas.	• Molecules with no charge. • Strong bonding inside each molecule but bonding between molecules is weak.
Macromolecules	• Hard. • High melting points.	• Diamond – drill heads. • Silicon dioxide.	• Giant covalent bond. • Huge lattices with millions of covalent bonds. • No weak forces to break.
Nanomaterial	• Very strong. • Huge surface area. • Conducts electricity.	• Nanoparticles – catalysts. • Nanotubes – reinforce tennis rackets, used in computer chips.	• Really tiny particles shaped like hollow balls or closed tubes. • Atoms form covalent bonds leaving free electrons.
Smart material	• Shape memory.	• Nitinol – spectacle frames.	• Can exist in two different solid forms. The molecules absorb energy to rearrange the atoms into a new form.

You need to be able to evaluate developments and applications of new materials, e.g. nanomaterials, smart materials.

New materials are being developed to provide us with materials that have advantageous properties and can therefore be very useful.

The development of nanomaterials is part of nanotechnology (the understanding and control of very small matter). Nanomaterials have many properties which means they have many uses in industry, for example, as industrial catalysts; their very, very small size means they have a large surface area in relation to their size.

Individual nanoparticles have different properties from the whole chemical. They can…

- fill plastics and coat surfaces
- absorb and reflect harmful ultraviolet rays in suncreams and cosmetics
- be added to glass to repel water to keep windows cleaner for longer
- be released in washing machines to clean clothes thoroughly
- be released in fridges to kill microorganisms and keep food fresher for longer
- be used in sensors, e.g. to test water purity.

Nanotubes which join nanoparticles are very strong. They conduct electricity so they can be used in electric circuits. However, it is important to remember that nanoparticles can be dangerous in certain circumstances, e.g. nanoparticles in water could be dangerous if they are drunk.

Nanotechnology has a wide variety of potential applications in biomedical, optical, and electronic fields. For example, nanotechnology could be used to create secure communication systems, detect and eradicate small tumours, help in the diagnosis of diseases, and in the development of microscopic surgery which would not leave scars.

Nanomaterials can be developed so they have useful properties such as being able to change shape or size as a result of being heated, or changing from a liquid to a solid when near a magnet. These are called smart materials and they can be categorised into different groups – electroactive, thermo-active, and magneto-active – depending on the trigger they respond to. Each type has a different property that can be altered and, therefore, they each have a different application.

Smart materials can be used in…

- sportswear because they are good thermal insulators as well as being lightweight, breathable and waterproof
- machine designs because they are very reliable, easy to control and fast acting.

New Material	Advantages	Disadvantages
Smart materials (A type of nanomaterial)	• Many different properties. • Many applications. • Easy to manipulate. • Many potential uses to investigate.	• Cost of developing new materials.
Nanomaterials	• Many applications. • Can reduce costs, e.g. when used as catalysts. • Have the potential for many more beneficial uses, especially in the medical industry.	• Difficult to engineer nanoparticles. • Can be dangerous in certain situations, e.g. if get into drinking water. • Is a danger that nanotechnology could be used to develop materials which could be a cause for concern.

12.3

How much can we make and how much do we need?

Atomic mass can be used to calculate the yield from a chemical reaction because we know that no atoms are lost or gained in a chemical reaction. To understand this, you need to know…

- how to find the mass number of an element
- how to find the relative atomic mass
- how to use the relative atomic mass to find the percentage of an element in a compound
- that some reactions can be reversible
- about the Haber process.

Mass Number and Atomic Number

Atoms of an element can be described very conveniently. For example, take the sodium atom…

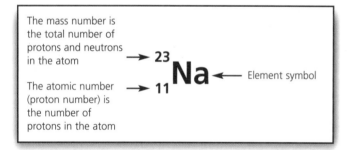

The mass number is the total number of protons and neutrons in the atom → ^{23}Na ← Element symbol

The atomic number (proton number) is the number of protons in the atom → $_{11}$

| Number of neutrons | = | Mass number | − | Atomic number |

The **atomic number** gives the number of protons, which is equal to the number of electrons. Because atoms have the same number of protons and electrons, they have no overall charge.

Examples

1 Hydrogen
$^{1}_{1}$H
1 proton
1 electron
0 neutrons (1-1)

2 Oxygen
$^{16}_{8}$O
8 protons
8 electrons
8 neutrons (16-8)

Although protons and electrons balance each other out because they have opposite charges, they do not have equal mass. Protons and neutrons (which together form the nucleus) each have a **relative mass** of 1, whereas the relative mass of an electron is almost nothing.

Atomic Particle	Relative Mass
Proton	1
Neutron	1
Electron	Very small (negligible)

Isotopes

All atoms of a particular element have the same number of protons; atoms of different elements have different numbers of protons.

However, some atoms of the same element can have different numbers of neutrons. These are called **isotopes**. They are easy to spot because they have the same atomic number but a different mass number.

Examples

1 Chlorine

$^{35}_{17}$Cl $^{37}_{17}$Cl

17 protons   17 protons
17 electrons   17 electrons
18 neutrons (35-17) 20 neutrons (37-17)

2 Carbon

$^{12}_{6}$C $^{13}_{6}$C $^{14}_{6}$C

6 protons   6 protons   6 protons
6 electrons   6 electrons   6 electrons
6 neutrons (12-6) 7 neutrons (13-6) 8 neutrons (14-6)

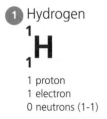

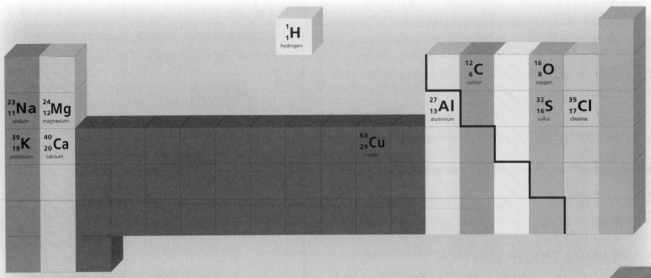

* In some versions of the periodic table this information may be presented slightly differently, e.g.

Relative Atomic Mass, A_r

Atoms are too small for their actual atomic mass to be of much use to us. To make things more manageable we use **relative atomic mass, A_r**. The relative atomic mass of an element is the same as its atomic mass.

Relative atomic mass $\longrightarrow$ $^{16}_{8}O$

 The relative atomic mass is the mass of a particular atom compared to a twelfth of the mass of a carbon atom (the ^{12}C isotope). It is an average value for all the isotopes of the element.

The mass number of the element conveniently doubles as the relative atomic mass, A_r, of the element. So, if we look at the mass numbers of the chemicals written in the periodic table above, we can see that carbon is 12 times heavier than hydrogen, but is only half as heavy as magnesium, which is three quarters as heavy as sulfur, which is twice as heavy as oxygen, and so on.

We can use this idea to calculate the relative formula mass of compounds.

Relative Formula Mass, M_r

The **relative formula mass (M_r)** of a compound is simply the relative atomic masses of all its elements added together. To calculate M_r, we need the formula of the compound, and the A_r of all the atoms involved.

Example 1

Using the data above, calculate the M_r of water, H_2O.

The formula... $\longrightarrow$ H_2O

Substitute the A_rs... $\longrightarrow$ $(2 \times 1) + 16$

The M_r $\longrightarrow$ $2 + 16 = 18$

Since water has an M_r of 18, it is 18 times heavier than a hydrogen atom, or one and a half times heavier than a carbon atom, or two thirds as heavy as an aluminium atom.

Example 2

Using the data above, calculate the M_r of potassium carbonate, K_2CO_3.

The formula... $\longrightarrow$ K_2CO_3

Substitute the A_rs... $\longrightarrow$ $(39 \times 2) + 12 + (16 \times 3)$

The M_r $\longrightarrow$ $78 + 12 + 48 = 138$

Unit 2

Calculating Percentage Mass of an Element in a Compound

If there are 12 left-handed pupils in a class of 30, you can work out the percentage of left-handers in the following way...

$$\frac{\text{Number of left-handers}}{\text{Total number in class}} \quad \textbf{X} \quad 100\%$$

In this case...

$$\frac{12}{30} \times 100\% = 40\%$$

You use exactly the same principle to calculate the percentage mass of an element in a compound, except this time we express it as...

$$\frac{\text{Relative mass of element in the compound}}{\text{Relative formula mass of compound (}M_r\text{)}} \quad \textbf{X} \quad 100\%$$

The mass of the compound is simply its relative formula mass and all you need to know is the formula of the compound and the relative atomic mass of all the atoms.

Example 1

Calculate the percentage mass of magnesium in magnesium oxide, MgO.

Relative mass of magnesium = 24

Relative formula mass (M_r) of MgO =

$$24 + 16 = 40$$

A_r Mg A_r O A_r MgO

Substituting into our formula...

$$\frac{\text{Relative mass of element}}{M_r \text{ of compound}} \times 100\%$$

$$\frac{24}{40} \times 100\% = \textbf{60\%}$$

Example 2

Calculate the percentage mass of potassium in potassium carbonate, K_2CO_3.

Relative mass of potassium = 39 x 2

Relative formula mass (M_r) of K_2CO_3 =

$$78 + 12 + 48 = 138$$

A_r K x 2 A_r C A_r O x 3 A_r K_2CO_3

Substituting into our formula...

$$\frac{\text{Relative mass of element}}{M_r \text{ of compound}} \times 100\%$$

$$\frac{78}{138} \times 100\% = \textbf{56.5\%}$$

(HT) Calculating the Empirical Formula of a Compound

The empirical formula of a compound is the simplest formula that represents the composition of the compound by mass.

Example

Find the simplest formula of an oxide of iron produced by reacting 1.12g of iron with 0.48g of oxygen (A_r Fe = 56, A_r O = 16).

Identify the mass of the elements in the compound...

Masses: Fe = 1.12, O = 0.48

Divide these masses by their relative atomic masses...

$$Fe = \frac{1.12}{56} = 0.02 \qquad O = \frac{0.48}{16} = 0.03$$

Identify the ratio of atoms in the compound...

Ratio =   0.02 : 0.03
     x 100 ↘   ↙ x 100
          2 : 3

Empirical formula = $\textbf{Fe}_2\textbf{O}_3$

The Mole

A **mole** (**mol**) is a measure of the number of particles (atoms or molecules) contained in a substance. One mole of any substance (element or compound) will always contain the same number of particles – six hundred thousand billion billion or 6×10^{23}. This is the relative formula mass of the substance.

If a substance is an element, the mass of one mole of the substance, called the molar mass (g/mol), is always equal to the relative atomic mass, A_r, of the substance in grams, for example…

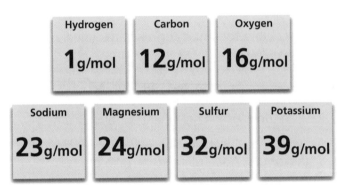

Hydrogen	Carbon	Oxygen
1g/mol	**12**g/mol	**16**g/mol

Sodium	Magnesium	Sulfur	Potassium
23g/mol	**24**g/mol	**32**g/mol	**39**g/mol

If a substance is a compound, the mass of one mole of the substance is always equal to the relative formula mass, M_r (A_rs of all its elements added together), of the substance in grams.

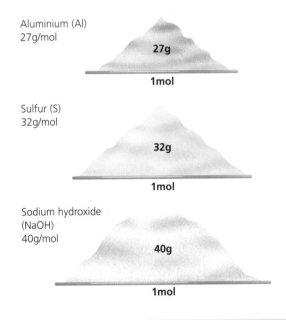

Aluminium (Al)
27g/mol

27g

1mol

Sulfur (S)
32g/mol

32g

1mol

Sodium hydroxide
(NaOH)
40g/mol

40g

1mol

A_r sodium + A_r hydrogen + A_r oxygen
= 23 + 1 + 16
= 40

Questions involving moles can be calculated using the following relationship. You need to remember this relationship because it will not be given to you in the examination.

$$\text{Number of moles of substance (mol)} = \frac{\text{Mass of substance (g)}}{\text{Mass of one mole (g/mol)}}$$

Example 1
Calculate the number of moles of carbon in 36g of the element.

Using the relationship…

$$\text{Number of moles of substance (mol)} = \frac{\text{Mass of substance (g)}}{\text{Mass of one mole (g/mol)}}$$

$$= \frac{36g}{12g/mol} \quad \leftarrow A_r \text{ carbon} = 12$$

$$= \textbf{3 moles}$$

Example 2
Calculate the number of moles of carbon dioxide in 33g of the gas.

Using the relationship…

$$\text{Number of moles of substance (mol)} = \frac{\text{Mass of substance (g)}}{\text{Mass of one mole (g/mol)}}$$

$$= \frac{33g}{44g/mol}$$

A_r carbon dioxide
= A_r carbon +
2 x A_r oxygen
= 12 + (2 x 16)
= 44

$$= \textbf{0.75 mole}$$

Example 3
Calculate the mass of 4 moles of sodium hydroxide.

Rearranging the relationship…

$$\text{Mass of substance (g)} = \text{Number of moles of substance (mol)} \times \text{Mass of one mole (g/mol)}$$

$$= 4mol \times 40g/mol$$

$$= \textbf{160g}$$

These calculations can also be done using ratios. It depends on how confident you are in your mathematical ability.

Calculating the Mass of a Product

Example

Calculate how much calcium oxide can be produced from 50kg of calcium carbonate. (Relative atomic masses: Ca = 40, C = 12, O = 16).

Write down the equation...

$$CaCO_3 \rightarrow CaO + CO_2$$

Work out the M_r of each substance...

$$40 + 12 + (3 \times 16) \rightarrow (40 + 16) + [12 + (2 \times 16)]$$

Check the total mass of reactants equals the total mass of the products. If they are not the same, check your work...

$$100 \rightarrow 56 + 44 \checkmark$$

Since the question only mentions calcium oxide and calcium carbonate, you can now ignore the carbon dioxide. You just need the ratio of mass of reactant to mass of product.

$$100 : 56$$

If 100kg of $CaCO_3$ produces 56kg of CaO, then 1kg of $CaCO_3$ produces $\frac{56}{100}$ kg of CaO, and 50kg of $CaCO_3$ produces $\frac{56}{100} \times 50$ = **28kg** of CaO.

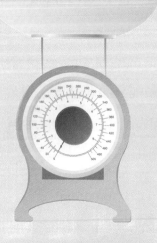

Calculating the Mass of a Reactant

Example

Calculate how much aluminium oxide is needed to produce 540 tonnes of aluminium. (Relative atomic masses: Al = 27, O = 16).

Write down the equation...

$$2Al_2O_3 \rightarrow 4Al + 3O_2$$

Work out the M_r of each substance...

$$2[(2 \times 27) + (3 \times 16)] \rightarrow (4 \times 27) + [3 \times (2 \times 16)]$$

Check the total mass of reactants equals the total mass of the products...

$$204 \rightarrow 108 + 96 \checkmark$$

Since the question only mentions aluminium oxide and aluminium, you can now ignore the oxygen. You just need the ratio of mass of reactant to mass of product.

$$204 : 108$$

If 204 tonnes of Al_2O_3 produces 108 tonnes of Al, then $\frac{204}{108}$ tonnes is needed to produce 1 tonne of Al, and $\frac{204}{108} \times 540$ tonnes is needed to produce 540 tonnes of Al, i.e. 1020 tonnes of Al_2O_3 is needed.

Yield

Atoms are never lost or gained in a chemical reaction. However, it is not always possible to obtain the calculated amount of the product because…

- if the reaction is reversible, it may not go to completion
- some product could be lost when it is separated from the reaction mixture
- there could be different ways for the reactants to behave in an expected reaction.

HT The amount of product obtained is called the **yield**. The **percentage yield** can be calculated by comparing the actual yield obtained from a reaction with the maximum theoretical yield.

$$\text{Percentage yield} = \frac{\text{Yield from reaction}}{\text{Maximum theoretical yield}} \times 100$$

Example

We know from the example on p.54 that you would expect to produce 28kg of calcium oxide (CaO) from 50kg of calcium carbonate ($CaCO_3$). This is the maximum theoretical yield.

A company heats 50kg of calcium carbonate in a kiln and obtains 22kg of calcium oxide.

Using the formula, the percentage yield is…

$$\text{Percentage yield} = \frac{22}{28} \times 100$$

$$= 78.6\%$$

Calculating Atom Economy

Because chemical reactions often produce more than one product, not all of the starting materials are converted into 'useful' products, e.g. products that can be used in industry.

Atom economy (atom utilisation) is a measure of the amounts of reactants that end up as useful products. This is an important calculation in industry, where the reaction conditions need to give economical and sustainable atom economy.

$$\text{Atom economy} = \frac{M_r \text{ of useful products}}{M_r \text{ of reactants}} \times 100$$

Example

Calcium carbonate ➤ Calcium oxide + Carbon dioxide

In this reaction, calcium oxide is the useful product because it can be used to produce slaked lime (see p.15). Carbon dioxide is also produced, but this is a waste product.

To calculate the atom economy of this reaction, first find the relative formula mass (M_r) of all the reactants and products.

$$CaCO_3 \blacktriangleright CaO + CO_2$$

M_r of $CaCO_3$ = $40 + 12 + (3 \times 16)$ = **100**

M_r of CaO = $40 + 16$ = **56**

M_r of CO_2 = $12 + (2 \times 16)$ = **44**

Using the equation…

$$\text{Atom economy} = \frac{56}{100} \times 100$$

$$= 56\%$$

44% will be wasted

Unit 2

Reversible Reactions

Some chemical reactions are **reversible**, i.e. the products can react to produce the original reactants.

A and B react to produce C and D, but also C and D can react to produce A and B. For example…

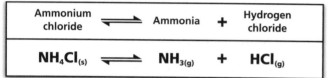

Solid ammonium chloride decomposes when heated to produce ammonia and hydrogen chloride gas, both of which are colourless (see diagram).

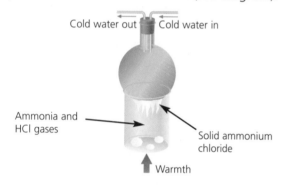

Cold water out — Cold water in

Ammonia and HCl gases

Solid ammonium chloride

Warmth

Ammonia reacts with hydrogen chloride gas to produce clouds of white ammonium chloride powder.

Production of Ammonia – the Haber Process

The raw materials for the Haber Process are…

- nitrogen – from the fractional distillation of liquid air
- hydrogen – from natural gas and steam.

The purified nitrogen and hydrogen are passed over an iron catalyst at a high temperature of about 450°C and a high pressure of about 200 atmospheres. Some of the hydrogen and nitrogen reacts to form ammonia. The ammonia produced can break down again into nitrogen and hydrogen.

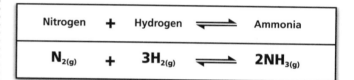

HT These reaction conditions are chosen to produce a reasonable yield of ammonia quickly, but even so, only some of the hydrogen and nitrogen react together to form ammonia.

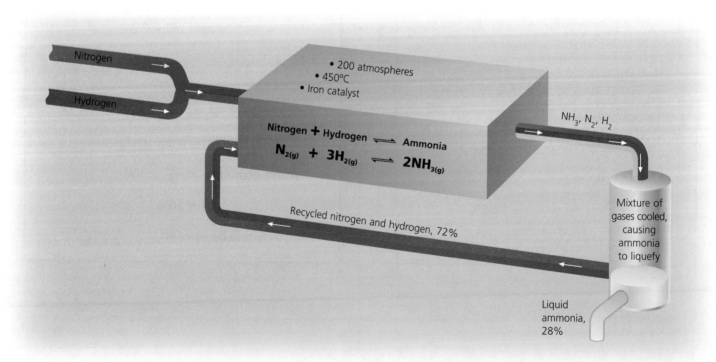

Nitrogen

Hydrogen

- 200 atmospheres
- 450°C
- Iron catalyst

Nitrogen + Hydrogen ⇌ Ammonia

$N_{2(g)} + 3H_{2(g)} \rightleftharpoons 2NH_{3(g)}$

NH_3, N_2, H_2

Recycled nitrogen and hydrogen, 72%

Mixture of gases cooled, causing ammonia to liquefy

Liquid ammonia, 28%

HT **You need to be able to calculate chemical quantities involving formula mass (Mᵣ) and calculate the atom economy for industrial processes and evaluate sustainable development issues relating to this economy.**

Ethyl ethanoate is used as a solvent in glues and nail polish removers. It is produced by the following reaction:

| Ethanoic acid | + | Ethanol | → | Ethyl ethanoate | + | Water |

$$C_2H_4O_{2(aq)} + C_2H_6O_{(aq)} \longrightarrow C_4H_8O_{2(aq)} + H_2O_{(l)}$$

To calculate the atom economy of this reaction we first need to work out the formula masses of the reactants and the useful product (ethyl ethanoate).

M_r of $C_2H_4O_2$ = (2 x 12) + (4 x 1) + (2 x 16) = **60**
M_r of C_2H_6O = (2 x 12) + (6 x 1) + 16 = **46**
M_r of $C_4H_8O_2$ = (4 x 12) + (8 x 1) + (2 x 16) = **88**

Now use the following formula to calculate the atom economy:

$$\text{Atom economy} = \frac{M_r \text{ of useful products}}{M_r \text{ of reactants}} \times 100\%$$

Atom economy = $\frac{88}{(60 + 46)}$ x 100% = 83% **17% will be wasted**

In industry, research scientists measure or calculate the amounts of materials used and produced in reactions to make sure the reactions are economical. If a reaction does not convert all of the reactants into useful products, there will be some wastage. As a result, the manufacturer might have to raise the sell-on price of the product, and this will have an impact on the retail price of all the final products it is used in.

It is important that chemical reactions which are part of industrial processes are as economical as possible, so that the product costs the people who need to buy it, as little as possible.

It is also important to plan for meeting the present needs of people without spoiling the environment. This is called a sustainable development. The Earth only has a finite supply of minerals, so it makes sense to only use as much as we need. Therefore, industries aim to use smaller amounts of raw materials and energy while creating less waste.

Scientists in industry look for ways to use the waste products so that they become useful by-products of the reaction.

The chemical industry examines its processes carefully to make sure that it...
- makes efficient use of energy
- reduces the hazards and risks of the chemicals it uses and makes
- reduces waste
- attempts to convert a high proportion of the atoms in the reactants into the products
- uses mainly renewable resources
- prevents pollution of the environment.

12.4

How can we control the rates of chemical reactions?

Controlling the rate of reactions is very important in industry. To understand this, you need to know...

- how to find the rate of a chemical reaction
- what factors affect the rate of reaction
- how catalysts are used to alter the rate of chemical reactions.

Rates of Reactions

Chemical reactions only occur when reacting particles collide with each other with sufficient energy. The minimum amount of energy required to cause a reaction is called the **activation energy**. There are four important factors which affect the rate of reaction:

- temperature
- concentration
- surface area
- use of a catalyst.

Temperature of the Reactants

Low Temperature	High Temperature
In a cold reaction mixture, the particles are moving quite slowly – the particles will collide with each other less often, with less energy, so fewer collisions will be successful. 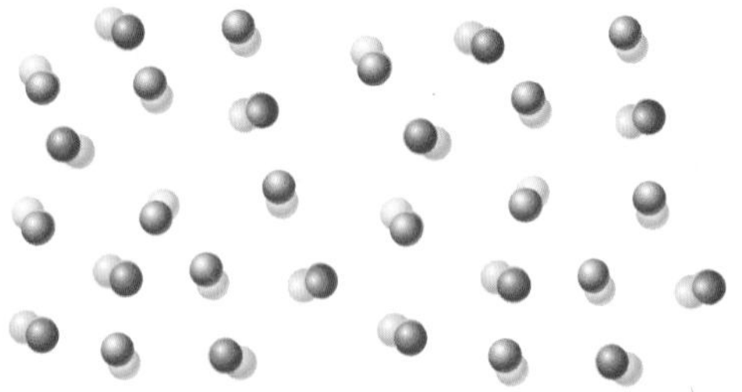	If we heat the reaction mixture, the particles will move more quickly – the particles will collide with each other more often, with greater energy, so many more collisions will be successful. 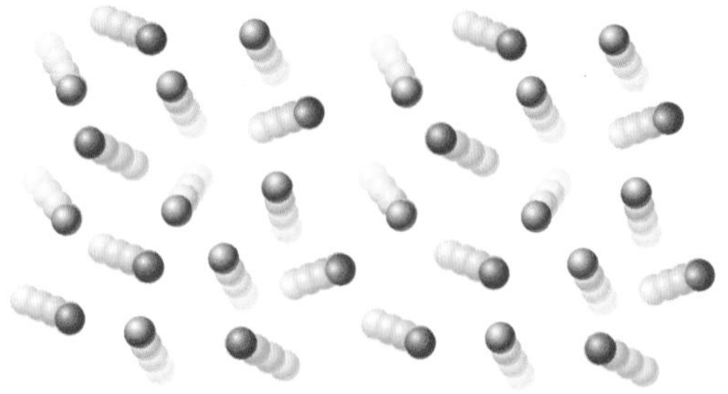

Concentration of the Dissolved Reactants

Low Concentration	High Concentration
In a reaction where one or both reactants are in low concentrations, the particles are spread out – the particles will collide with each other less often resulting in fewer successful collisions. 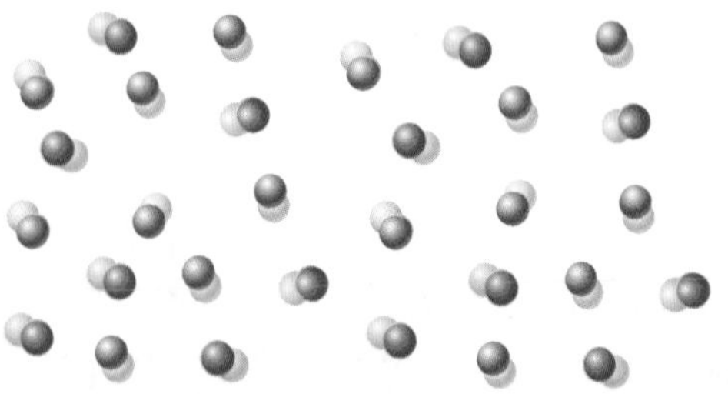	Where there are high concentrations of one or both reactants, the particles are crowded close together – the particles will collide with each other more often, resulting in many more successful collisions. 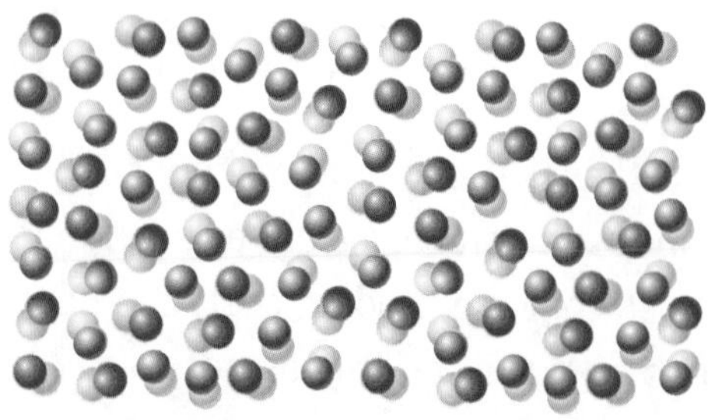

We see a similar effect when the reactants are gases. As the pressure on a gas is increased, the particles are pushed closer together so they collide more often and the reaction is faster.

Rate of reaction increases

Concentrations of solutions are given in **moles per cubic decimetre (mol/dm³)**. Equal volumes of solutions of the same molar concentration contain the same number of moles of solute, i.e. the same number of particles.

Equal volumes of gases at the same temperature and pressure contain the same number of molecules.

Surface Area of Solid Reactants

Large particles have a small surface area in relation to their volume, so fewer particles are exposed and available for collisions. This means fewer collisions and a slower reaction. Small particles have a large surface area in relation to their volume, so more particles are exposed and available for collisions. This means more collisions and a faster reaction.

Large Particles	Small Particles
• Small surface area. • Fewer collisions. • Reaction rate is slow.	• Large surface area. • More collisions. • Reaction rate is faster.

Using a Catalyst

A **catalyst** is a substance which increases the rate of a chemical reaction without being used up or altered in the process. It can be used over and over again to increase the rate at which reactants are converted into products.

A catalyst lowers the amount of energy needed for a successful collision, so more collisions will be successful and the reaction will be faster. Also, it provides a surface for the molecules to attach to, thereby increasing their chances of bumping into each other.

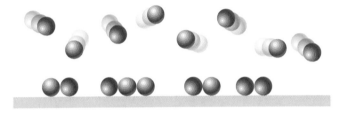

Catalysts are specific to reactions, i.e. different reactions need different catalysts, e.g. the cracking of hydrocarbons uses broken pottery; the manufacture of ammonia (Haber process) uses iron.

Increasing the rates of chemical reactions is important in industry because it helps to reduce costs.

Catalysts used in the cracking of hydrocarbons

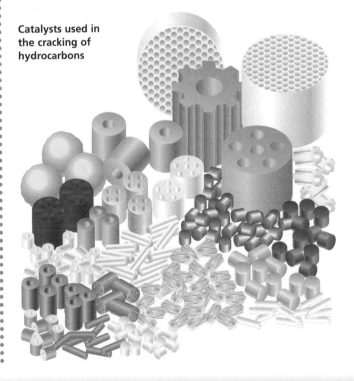

Analysing the Rate of Reaction

The rate of a chemical reaction can be found by...
- measuring the amount of reactants used
- measuring the amount of products formed.

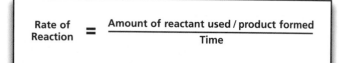

For example, the decomposition of hydrogen peroxide using manganese (IV) oxide.

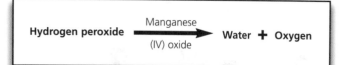

You could measure the amount of reactant used by weighing the mixture before and after the reaction takes place. In the case of hydrogen peroxide, oxygen is released from the mixture so the mass of the mixture will decrease.

You could use a gas syringe to measure the volume of gas produced, in this case, oxygen.

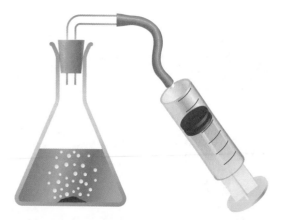

To test for oxygen gas, insert a glowing splint into a jar of collected gas. Oxygen will relight a glowing splint.

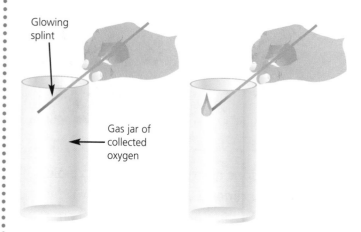

Glowing splint

Gas jar of collected oxygen

Graphs can then be plotted to show the progress of a chemical reaction – there are three things to remember...

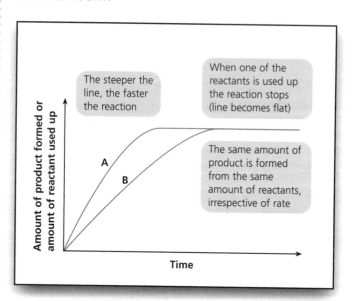

The steeper the line, the faster the reaction

When one of the reactants is used up the reaction stops (line becomes flat)

The same amount of product is formed from the same amount of reactants, irrespective of rate

Reaction **A** is faster than reaction **B**. This could be because...
- the surface area of the solid reactants in **A** is greater than in **B**
- the temperature of reaction **A** is greater than reaction **B**
- the concentration of the solution in **A** is greater than in **B**
- a catalyst is used in reaction **A** but not in reaction **B**.

You need to be able to interpret graphs showing the amount of product formed (or reactant used up) with time, in terms of the rate of the reaction.

The rate of a reaction is the amount of reactant used up or product made, in a given time. One of the factors which affects the rate of reaction is the concentration of dissolved reactants.

An investigation was carried out to find out how different concentrations of hydrochloric acid affect the rate of reaction between marble chips and hydrochloric acid. The reaction which takes place is:

Calcium carbonate + Dilute hydrochloric acid $\longrightarrow$ Calcium chloride + Carbon dioxide + Water

$$CaCO_{3(s)} + 2HCl_{(aq)} \longrightarrow CaCl_{2(aq)} + CO_{2(g)} + H_2O_{(l)}$$

The table below shows how the acid was diluted.

Volume of acid (cm³)	Volume of water (cm³)	Graph number
0	50	No reaction
10	40	1
20	30	2
30	20	3
40	10	4
50	0	5

Each reaction was started and readings of the volume of carbon dioxide gas produced were taken continuously over 10 minutes. The volume was recorded every 30 seconds. This method of collecting results or data is called a continuous method. This method measures the rate of the product made.

A graph was plotted of the volume of carbon dioxide produced against time for each concentration of the hydrochloric acid.

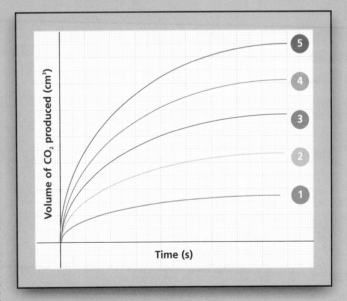

The rate of reaction can be worked out from the graphs. We can see that the most concentrated solution (graph 5) has the steepest curve on the graph, which means it produced CO_2 the quickest. Graph 1 shows the least steep curve which tells us that this reaction was the slowest at producing CO_2.

How Science Works

You need to be able to explain and evaluate the development, advantages and disadvantages of using catalysts in industrial processes.

Catalysts are substances which speed up the rate of a reaction whilst remaining chemically unchanged and without being used up, which means they can be used repeatedly.

As this makes the reaction faster, and the product is produced more quickly, this can save an enormous amount of money in labour and energy costs. Greater quantities of the product can then be made quickly to meet further demand.

Catalysts can be used to get the reaction to take place at lower temperatures, which means less activation energy is needed. This makes it easier for the reaction to start and reduces the energy requirements of the process which is good for sustainable development and also reduces cost.

Catalysts have been used in industrial processes for years. Different reactions require different catalysts so a number of catalysts have been developed.

Many transition metals are used as catalysts, e.g. iron is used in the production of ammonia, platinum in the production of nitric acid, and silica / aluminium oxide in the production of alkenes (which make plastics).

As technology has become more advanced, scientists are able to work with smaller and smaller structures, such as nanomaterials. Their very, very small size means they have a large surface area in relation to their size, which makes them ideal to be used as industrial catalysts.

However, it is important to remember that different reactions require different catalysts and they are very expensive to buy. They also need to be removed from the product and cleaned regularly otherwise they become 'poisoned' and will not work properly.

The table alongside lists the advantages and disadvantages of using catalysts.

Nanomaterials used as industrial catalysts

Advantages
• They increase the rate of reaction which speeds up industrial processes.
• They reduce the costs of industrial processes.
• They save energy.
• They help sustainable development.
• They can be used over and over again.

Disadvantages
• They are expensive.
• They need to be cleaned regularly to prevent them becoming poisoned.

12.5

Do chemical reactions always release energy?

Chemical reactions either take in or give out energy. Energy requirements and emissions need to be carefully considered in industry. To understand this, you need to know…

- what the terms 'exothermic' and 'endothermic' mean
- how equilibrium can be reached in a reversible reaction
- that the yield depends on the conditions of the reaction.

When chemical reactions occur, energy is transferred to or from the surroundings, so many chemical reactions are accompanied by a temperature change.

Exothermic Reactions

These reactions are accompanied by a temperature rise. They are known as **exothermic** reactions because they transfer heat energy to the surroundings, i.e. they give out heat. Combustion is a common example of an exothermic reaction, e.g.

| Methane (natural gas) | + Oxygen | → | Carbon dioxide | + Water + | Heat energy |

$$CH_{4(g)} + 2O_{2(g)} \longrightarrow CO_{2(g)} + 2H_2O_{(l)}$$

It is not only reactions between fuels and oxygen which are exothermic. Neutralising alkalis with acids gives out heat too, as do many oxidation reactions.

HT If the temperature is raised, the yield decreases. If the temperature is lowered, the yield increases.

Endothermic Reactions

These reactions are accompanied by a fall in temperature. They are known as **endothermic** reactions because heat energy is transferred from the surroundings, i.e. they take in heat. Dissolving ammonium nitrate crystals in water is an endothermic reaction…

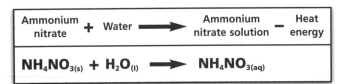

| Ammonium nitrate | + Water | → | Ammonium nitrate solution | − | Heat energy |

$$NH_4NO_{3(s)} + H_2O_{(l)} \longrightarrow NH_4NO_{3(aq)}$$

Thermal decomposition is also an example of an endothermic reaction.

HT If the temperature is raised, the yield increases. If the temperature is lowered, the yield decreases.

Gaseous Reactions

In gaseous reactions, an increase in pressure favours the reaction which produces the least number of molecules.

*N.B. These factors above, along with reaction rates, determine the optimum conditions in industrial processes. An important example is the **Haber process** (see page 56).*

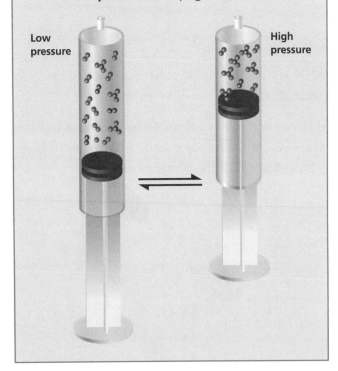

Low pressure   High pressure

Unit 2

Reversible Reactions

If a reaction is reversible and it is exothermic in one direction then it follows that it is endothermic in the opposite direction, with the same amount of energy being transferred in each case. An example of this is when hydrated copper sulfate is gently heated.

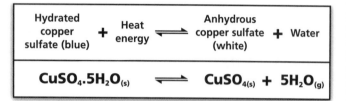

| Hydrated copper sulfate (blue) | + | Heat energy | ⇌ | Anhydrous copper sulfate (white) | + | Water |

$$CuSO_4.5H_2O_{(s)} \rightleftharpoons CuSO_{4(s)} + 5H_2O_{(g)}$$

If water is added to white anhydrous copper sulfate, blue hydrated copper sulfate is formed as heat is given out.

Hydrated Copper Sulfate

Anhydrous Copper Sulfate

Blue crystals of hydrated copper sulfate become white anhydrous copper sulfate on heating, as water is removed.

The reverse reaction above can be used as a test for water where the colour change from white to blue is an indication of the presence of water.

Reversible Reactions in Closed Systems

When a reversible reaction occurs in a closed system (where no reactants are added and no products are removed) then an equilibrium is achieved where the reactions occur at exactly the same rate in both directions. The relative amounts of all the reacting substances at equilibrium depend on the conditions of the reaction. If we take the reaction...

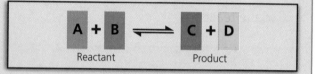

If the forward reaction (the reaction that produces the products C and D) is endothermic then...

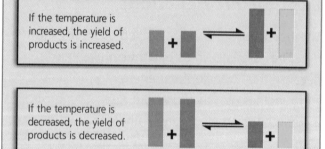

If the forward reaction is exothermic then...

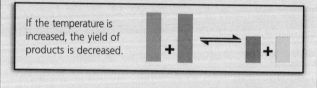

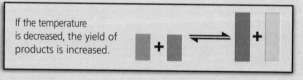

Even though a reversible reaction may not go to completion, it may still be used efficiently in an industrial process, e.g. the Haber process (see p.56).

Sustainable Development

It is important for sustainable development and economic reasons to minimise energy use and wastage in industrial processes.

Non-vigorous conditions mean less energy is used and less is released into the environment, but the reaction is less efficient.

Effect of Varying Conditions on Reversible Reactions

The manufacture of ammonia is a reversible reaction, involving energy transfers associated with the breaking and formation of chemical bonds.

$$N_{2(g)} + 3H_{2(g)} \xrightleftharpoons[\text{Endothermic}]{\text{Exothermic}} 2NH_{3(g)}$$

Less energy is needed to break the bonds between the nitrogen and hydrogen molecules than is released in the formation of the ammonia molecules.

Effect of Temperature

At low temperatures, the production of ammonia (the forward reaction), which is an exothermic reaction, is favoured, i.e. the yield of ammonia is increased.

Increasing the temperature increases the rate of reaction equally in both directions, therefore high temperatures make ammonia form faster, but also break down faster.

Effect of Pressure

Increasing the pressure favours the smaller volume. Therefore high pressure favours the production of ammonia, since four molecules are being changed into two molecules, and increases the yield.

A Compromise Solution

Altering the temperature and pressure can have a big impact on the production of ammonia in the Haber process. The conditions have to be chosen very carefully to be economically viable and to make sure they can meet demand.

The formation of ammonia is exothermic so a low temperature increases the yield, but the reaction is very slow. A high temperature makes the reaction faster, but produces a lower yield. So a compromise is reached.

The volume of ammonia produced is less than the total volume of the reactants (nitrogen and hydrogen) so a high pressure favours the production of ammonia, but this is very expensive. A low pressure is more affordable, but this produces a low yield. So yet again a compromise is reached.

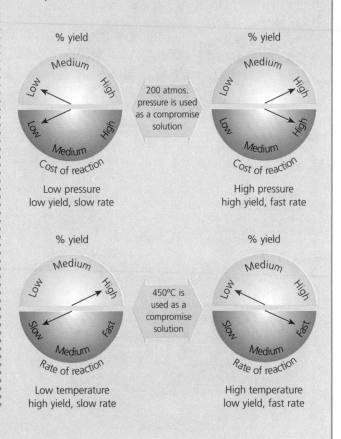

Low pressure low yield, slow rate

High pressure high yield, fast rate

200 atmos. pressure is used as a compromise solution

Low temperature high yield, slow rate

High temperature low yield, fast rate

450°C is used as a compromise solution

How Science Works

You need to be able to evaluate the conditions used in industrial processes in terms of energy requirements.

Chemical reactions involve energy transfers. Many chemical reactions involve the release of energy and some reactions take in energy. In industrial processes, energy requirements and emissions need to be considered both for economic reasons and for sustainable development. It is important that energy is not wasted in industrial processes. Non-vigorous conditions mean less energy is used and less is lost into the environment.

The conditions used in any industrial process must be considered in terms of the yield of the product. There might need to be a compromise between maximum yield and speed of reaction.

It could be more economical to wait longer for the sake of a higher yield.

Using a catalyst

Adding a catalyst lowers the activation energy for a reaction so lower temperatures can be used. This usually results in a saving in energy costs.

Changing Pressure or Temperature

Raising the temperature in a chemical reaction increases the energy of the particles involved and they move faster. If they move faster more collisions between the particles take place and this means the reaction goes faster. Sometimes, however, the higher temperature can encourage some of the products made to break up and so this is not favourable to the forward reaction. A compromise temperature is then chosen for the process to proceed at.

Increasing the pressure also increases the reaction because the particles have less room to spread out in, so they collide much more often.

When evaluating the methods used in industry, we need to take into account the amount of energy needed for a reaction, the percentage yield that each method makes, the cost, and the impact on the environment.

Using a Catalyst

Advantages
- Reduces activation energy needed for a reaction.
- Speeds up reaction.
- Reduces cost of reaction.

Disadvantages
- Different reactions need different catalysts.
- Catalyst needs to be removed and cleaned regularly to prevent it from becoming poisoned.
- Purchasing catalysts can be costly.

Increasing Pressure or Temperature

Advantages
- Increases rate of reaction.
- May get a higher percentage yield.

Disadvantages
- Reaction would cost more.
- Percentage yield will only increase up to a certain point.

12.6

How can we use ions in solutions?

Ionic compounds can be used in electrolysis to produce many useful products. Oxidation–reduction reactions involve the transfer of electrons. Ionic solutions can be used to make soluble and insoluble salts. To understand this, you need to know…

- the state symbols
- the properties of ions in solutions
- about electrolysis and its uses
- how to make soluble and insoluble salts
- what the pH scale measures.

State Symbols

The states of the compounds and elements involved in reactions are shown using the state symbols: (s) solid, (l) liquid, (aq) aqueous solution and (g) gas. An aqueous solution is produced when a substance is dissolved in water.

Electrolysis

Electrolysis is the breaking down of a compound containing ions (charged particles) into its elements using an electrical current. During electrolysis, ions gain or lose electrons at the electrodes, forming electrically neutral atoms or molecules which are then released (i.e. they have no charge).

Principles of Electrolysis

Ionic substances are chemical compounds that allow an electric current to flow through them when they are molten or dissolved in water.

These compounds contain negative and positive ions and the electric current is due to negatively charged ions moving to the positive electrode and positively charged ions moving to the negative electrode. When this happens, simpler substances are released at the two electrodes. This is **electrolysis**.

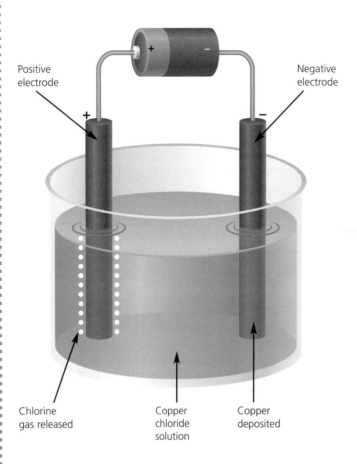

Positive electrode

Negative electrode

Chlorine gas released

Copper chloride solution

Copper deposited

If there is a mixture of ions in the solution, the products formed depend on the reactivity of the elements involved. For example, in the electrolysis of copper chloride solution, the simple substances released are copper at the negative electrode and chlorine gas at the positive electrode.

Redox Reactions

During electrolysis, positively charged ions gain electrons at the negative electrode. This gain of electrons is known as **reduction**.

At the positive electrode, negatively charged ions lose electrons. This loss of electrons is known as **oxidation**.

A chemical reaction where both reduction and oxidation occurs is called a **redox** reaction. It will help you to remember the above if you remember the word **oilrig**.

- **O**xidation **I**s **L**oss of electrons (**OIL**)
- **R**eduction **I**s **G**ain of electrons (**RIG**)

Unit 2

Purification of Copper by Electrolysis

Copper can easily be extracted by reduction but when it is needed in a pure form it is purified by electrolysis. For electrolysis to take place…

- the positive electrode needs to be made of impure copper
- the negative electrode needs to be made of pure copper
- the solution must contain copper ions.

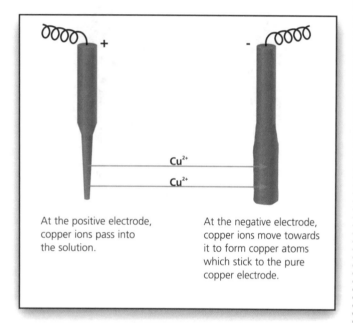

At the positive electrode, copper ions pass into the solution.

At the negative electrode, copper ions move towards it to form copper atoms which stick to the pure copper electrode.

Consequently, the negative electrode gets bigger and bigger as the positive electrode seems to dissolve away to nothing. The impurities in the positive electrode simply fall to the bottom as the process takes place.

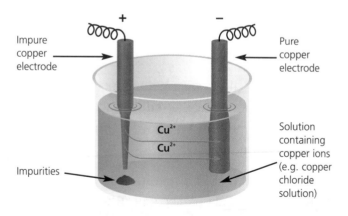

Impure copper electrode

Pure copper electrode

Impurities

Solution containing copper ions (e.g. copper chloride solution)

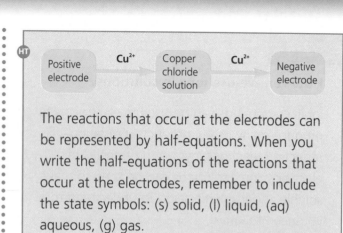

The reactions that occur at the electrodes can be represented by half-equations. When you write the half-equations of the reactions that occur at the electrodes, remember to include the state symbols: (s) solid, (l) liquid, (aq) aqueous, (g) gas.

The following half-equations show the reactions that occur at the electrodes during the electrolysis of copper. Remember that chlorine exists as molecules.

At the negative electrode:

$$Cu^{2+} + 2e^- \longrightarrow Cu_{(s)}$$

At the positive electrode:

$$2Cl^- \longrightarrow Cl_{2(g)} + 2e^-$$

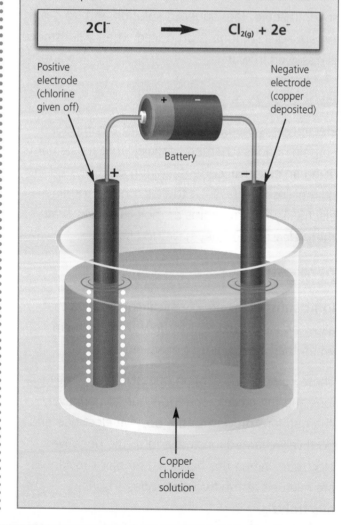

Positive electrode (chlorine given off)

Negative electrode (copper deposited)

Battery

Copper chloride solution

Industrial Electrolysis of Sodium Chloride Solution (Brine)

Sodium chloride (common salt) is a compound of an alkali metal and a halogen. It is found in large quantities in the sea and in underground deposits. Electrolysis of sodium chloride solution produces some very important reagents for the chemical industry...

- chlorine gas at the positive electrode
- hydrogen gas at the negative electrode
- sodium hydroxide solution which is passed out of the cell.

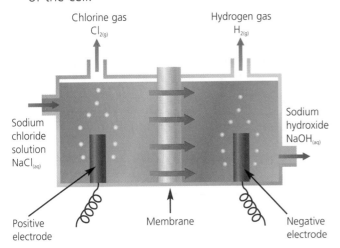

The products of the electrolysis of brine have many uses:

- Chlorine is used to kill bacteria in drinking water and swimming pools and to manufacture hydrochloric acid, disinfectants, bleach and the plastic PVC.
- Hydrogen is used in the manufacture of ammonia and margarine.
- Sodium hydroxide is used in the manufacture of soap, paper and ceramics.

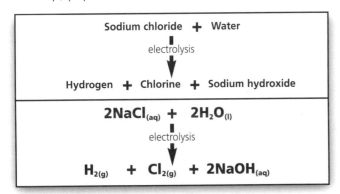

A simple laboratory test for chlorine is that it bleaches damp litmus paper, i.e. the chlorine removes the colour.

Indicators

Indicators are useful dyes which change colour depending on whether they are in acidic or alkaline solutions.

Some are simple substances such as litmus, which changes from red to blue or vice versa. Others are mixtures of dyes, such as universal indicator, which show a range of colours to indicate just how acidic or alkaline a substance is.

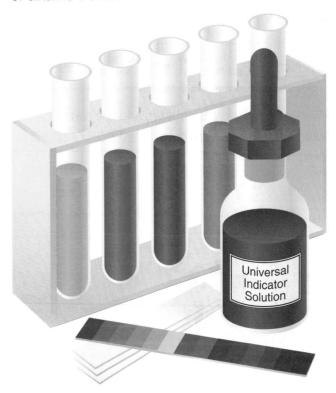

pH Scale

The pH scale is a measure of the acidity or alkalinity of an aqueous solution, across a 14-point scale.

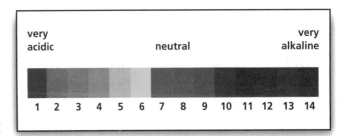

When substances dissolve in water, they dissociate into their individual ions...

- hydroxide ions ($OH^-_{(aq)}$) make solutions alkaline
- hydrogen ions ($H^+_{(aq)}$) make solutions acidic.

Neutralisation

Acids and alkalis are **chemical opposites**, so if they are added together in the correct amounts they can 'cancel' each other out. This is because the hydrogen ions react with hydroxide ions to produce water.

$$H^+_{(aq)} + OH^-_{(aq)} \longrightarrow H_2O_{(l)}$$

This is called neutralisation because the solution which remains has a neutral pH of 7.

Acid	+	Alkaline hydroxide solution		Neutral salt solution	+	Water

We can see this working if we add the same volumes of HCl (a strong acid) and KOH (a strong alkali) together.

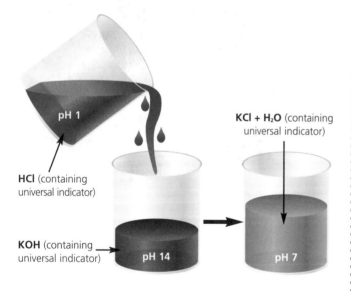

pH 1
HCl (containing universal indicator)
KOH (containing universal indicator)
pH 14
KCl + H₂O (containing universal indicator)
pH 7

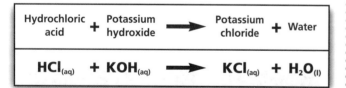

Hydrochloric acid	+	Potassium hydroxide		Potassium chloride	+	Water
$HCl_{(aq)}$	+	$KOH_{(aq)}$		$KCl_{(aq)}$	+	$H_2O_{(l)}$

Again, if we look at what happens to the hydrogen ions $H^+_{(aq)}$ and the hydroxide ions $OH^-_{(aq)}$ in the acid and alkali, we can see that they react to form water:

$$H^+_{(aq)} + OH^-_{(aq)} \longrightarrow H_2O_{(l)}$$

Ammonia is an alkaline gas which dissolves in water to make an alkaline solution. Its main use is in the production of fertilisers to increase the nitrogen content of the soil. Ammonia neutralises nitric acid to produce ammonium nitrate (a fertiliser rich in nitrogen), which is sometimes known as 'nitram' (nitrate of ammonia). The aqueous ammonium nitrate is then evaporated to dryness.

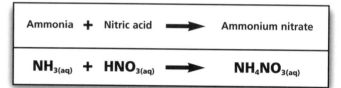

Ammonia	+	Nitric acid		Ammonium nitrate
$NH_{3(aq)}$	+	$HNO_{3(aq)}$		$NH_4NO_{3(aq)}$

Nitrogen-based fertilisers are important chemicals as they increase the yields of crops. However, nitrates can create problems if they find their way into streams, rivers or groundwater, as they can upset the natural balance and contaminate our drinking water.

Soluble Salts from Metals

Metals which react with dilute acid form a metal salt and hydrogen. **Salt** is a word used to describe any metal compound made when a reaction takes place between a metal and an acid.

Metal	+	Acid		Salt	+	Hydrogen

However, some metals react more vigorously than others...

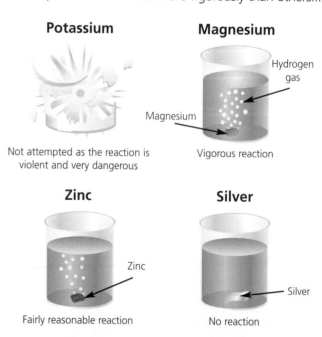

Potassium

Not attempted as the reaction is violent and very dangerous

Magnesium

Hydrogen gas
Magnesium
Vigorous reaction

Zinc

Zinc
Fairly reasonable reaction

Silver

Silver
No reaction

Soluble Salts from Insoluble Bases

Bases are the oxides and hydroxides of metals. Those which are soluble are called **alkalis**.

Unfortunately, the oxides and hydroxides of transition metals are insoluble, which means that preparing their salts is a little less straightforward.

The metal oxide or hydroxide is added to an acid until no more will react. The excess metal oxide or hydroxide is then filtered off to leave a solution of the salt which can then be evaporated to dryness.

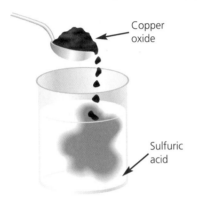

Add copper oxide to sulfuric acid

Filter to remove any unreacted copper oxide

Evaporate to leave behind blue crystals of the 'salt' copper sulfate

This can be written more generally as…

Ammonia also dissolves in water to produce an alkaline solution. This can be neutralised with acids to produce ammonium salts, which are important as fertilisers (see p.70).

	Hydrochloric Acid	Sulfuric Acid	Nitric Acid
Ammonium Hydroxide	Ammonium chloride and water	Ammonium sulfate and water	Ammonium nitrate and water

Salts of Alkali Metals

Compounds of alkali metals, called salts, can be made by reacting solutions of their hydroxides (which are alkaline) with a particular acid. This is called a neutralisation reaction (see p.70) and can be represented as follows:

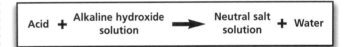

The salt produced depends on the metal in the alkali and the acid used.

	Hydrochloric Acid	Sulfuric Acid	Nitric Acid
Sodium Hydroxide	Sodium chloride and water	Sodium sulfate and water	Sodium nitrate and water
Potassium Hydroxide	Potassium chloride and water	Potassium sulfate and water	Potassium nitrate and water

Insoluble Salts

Insoluble salts can be made by mixing appropriate solutions of ions so that a solid substance (precipitate) is formed. Precipitation can be used to remove unwanted ions from solution, e.g. softening hard water. The calcium (or magnesium) ions are precipitated out as insoluble calcium (or magnesium) carbonate.

How Science Works

You need to be able to predict the results of electrolysing solutions of ions.

Ionic substances conduct electricity and can be broken down when they are molten or in solution. The process of electrolysis uses electrical energy to break down these substances and is used to manufacture important chemical substances that we use in our everyday lives.

The following rules can be used to predict the results of electrolysing solutions.

- If a metal is high in the Reactivity Series, hydrogen is produced at the negative electrode instead of the metal.
- If the metal is below hydrogen in the Reactivity Series, the metal is produced.
- If you have concentrated solutions of chlorides, bromides or iodides then chlorine, bromine or iodine is produced at the positive electrode. With other common negative ions oxygen is produced.

HT **You need to be able to complete and balance supplied half-equations for the reactions occurring at the electrodes during electrolysis.**

We can write and balance half-equations to show what happens at each electrode during the electrolysis. For example, for the electrolysis of brine (salt water). Write down a word equation…

Sodium chloride + Water $\xrightarrow{\text{electrolysis}}$ Sodium hydroxide + Chlorine + Hydrogen

$$2NaCl_{(aq)} + 2H_2O_{(l)} \longrightarrow 2NaOH_{(aq)} + Cl_{2(g)} + H_{2(g)}$$

Then look at what happens at the positive electrode…

$$2Cl^-_{(aq)} \longrightarrow Cl_{2(g)} + 2e^-$$

… and what happens at the negative electrode…

$$2H^+_{(aq)} + 2e^- \longrightarrow H_{2(g)}$$

The sodium ions (Na^+) and the hydroxide ions (OH^-) combine to produce sodium hydroxide ($NaOH$).

You need to be able to explain and evaluate processes that use the principles described in this unit.

The process of electrolysis uses electrical energy to break down ionic substances, which are molten or in solution, into elements. This process is important industrially as it is used to manufacture important chemical substances we need for our everyday lives.

Example

The electrolysis of sea water or brine (see p.69) gives us large quantities of hydrogen gas, chlorine and sodium hydroxide solution. These products are also used as the starting point for other useful products such as disinfectants, fertilisers and soap.

The process is very expensive because of all the energy which is required to bring about the change.

Advantages

- Three very important materials (hydrogen, chlorine and sodium hydroxide) are produced from one raw material (brine).
- Brine is a renewable source which is readily available and cheap.
- The products of the electrolysis of brine are used in many industries to make a large variety of products.
- As all the products are useful there is minimal waste.

Disadvantages

- The process of electrolysis is very expensive as it depends upon electrical energy to work.
- The production of electrical energy in traditional power stations adds to the pollution in the atmosphere.
- Hydrogen and chlorine can be produced by other methods much more cheaply.

You need to be able to suggest methods to make a named salt.

Example

FACTSHEET

There are two main groups of salts: soluble salts and insoluble salts. Insoluble salts are made from solutions of ions. Two solutions of soluble salts can react to make an insoluble salt and a new soluble salt. The insoluble salt separates as a solid precipitate and the new soluble salt stays in the solution.

Solubility rules for salts:
- all group 1 metal compounds are soluble
- all nitrates are soluble
- all chlorides are soluble except silver and lead
- all sulfates are soluble except calcium, barium and lead
- all carbonates are insoluble except group 1 metal carbonates.

Acids which make salts:
- hydrochloric acid makes chlorides
- sulfuric acid makes sulfates
- nitric acid makes nitrates.

Copper Sulfate

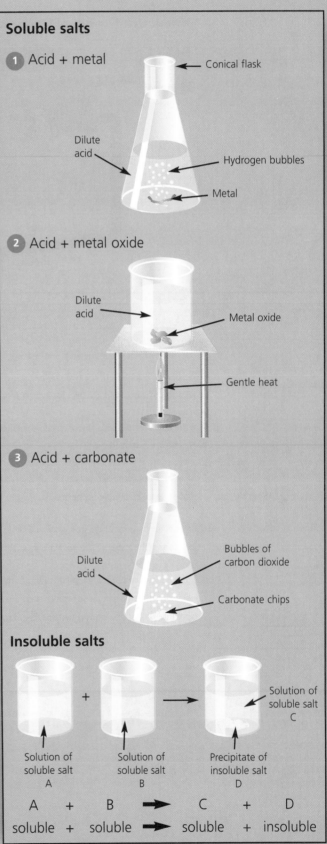

Soluble salts

1 Acid + metal
- Conical flask
- Dilute acid
- Hydrogen bubbles
- Metal

2 Acid + metal oxide
- Dilute acid
- Metal oxide
- Gentle heat

3 Acid + carbonate
- Dilute acid
- Bubbles of carbon dioxide
- Carbonate chips

Insoluble salts

Solution of soluble salt A + Solution of soluble salt B → Solution of soluble salt C + Precipitate of insoluble salt D

A + B → C + D
soluble + soluble → soluble + insoluble

Using the information above, suggest which method (shown right) you would use to make copper sulfate and silver chloride and explain your reasoning.

Copper sulfate is a soluble salt. Copper will not react with acid as it is an unreactive metal. The salt cannot be made from the metal and acid, so we can use the metal oxide and acid. Sulfuric acid makes sulfates.

The excess solid is then filtered off and the solution of copper sulfate is heated gently to evaporate some of the water. The concentrated solution is then left to crystallise.

Silver chloride is an insoluble salt. The method to make silver chloride will use the soluble salt silver nitrate and the soluble salt sodium chloride. Add the two soluble salts together and the insoluble silver chloride will precipitate. The insoluble precipitate can be removed from the solution of sodium nitrate by filtration. The precipitate is then left to dry at room temperature.

Example Questions

For Unit 2, you will have to complete one written paper with structured questions.

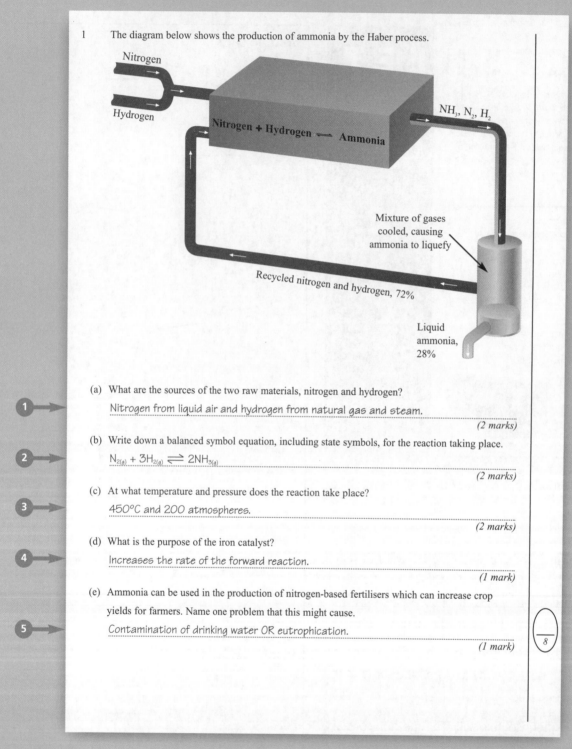

1   The diagram below shows the production of ammonia by the Haber process.

Nitrogen

Hydrogen

Nitrogen + Hydrogen ⇌ Ammonia

NH_3, N_2, H_2

Mixture of gases cooled, causing ammonia to liquefy

Recycled nitrogen and hydrogen, 72%

Liquid ammonia, 28%

(a) What are the sources of the two raw materials, nitrogen and hydrogen?

   1 → Nitrogen from liquid air and hydrogen from natural gas and steam.

   (2 marks)

(b) Write down a balanced symbol equation, including state symbols, for the reaction taking place.

   2 → $N_{2(g)} + 3H_{2(g)} \rightleftharpoons 2NH_{3(g)}$

   (2 marks)

(c) At what temperature and pressure does the reaction take place?

   3 → 450°C and 200 atmospheres.

   (2 marks)

(d) What is the purpose of the iron catalyst?

   4 → Increases the rate of the forward reaction.

   (1 mark)

(e) Ammonia can be used in the production of nitrogen-based fertilisers which can increase crop yields for farmers. Name one problem that this might cause.

   5 → Contamination of drinking water OR eutrophication.

   (1 mark)

8

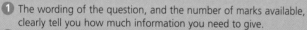

1 The wording of the question, and the number of marks available, clearly tell you how much information you need to give.

2 Read the question carefully. You could lose marks here if you forget the state symbols.

3 Don't forget to include units (e.g. °C) for all measurements!

4 You only need to know what a catalyst does to answer this question.

5 The question only requires one example, but there are several possible answers.

Acid – a compound that has a pH value of lower than 7

Alkali – a compound that has a pH value higher than 7

Alkali metals – elements in Group 1 of the periodic table – lithium, sodium, potassium, rubidium, caesium and francium

Atomic number – the number of protons an element has in the nucleus of its atom; the mass of an atom compared to the mass of a hydrogen atom

Covalent bonding – a bond between two atoms in which both atoms share one electron

Electrodes – pieces of metal or carbon which allow electric current to enter and leave during electrolysis

Electrolysis – the process by which an electric current causes a solution to undergo chemical decomposition

Electron – a negatively charged particle found outside the nucleus of an atom

Endothermic reaction – a reaction which takes in heat from the surroundings

Exothermic reaction – a reaction which gives off heat

Halogens – elements in Group 7 of the periodic table – fluorine, chlorine, bromine, iodine and astatine

Ionic bonding – the process by which two or more atoms lose or gain electrons to become charged ions

Mole (mol) – the molar mass of a substance, i.e. the mass in grammes of 6×10^{23} particles

Nanomaterials – materials with a very small grain size

Neutralisation – a reaction between an acid and a base which forms a neutral solution

Neutron – a particle found in the nucleus of an atom; has no electric charge

Noble gas – an inert, colourless gas, e.g. helium, neon, krypton, xenon or radon

Nucleus – the small central core of an atom, consisting of protons and neutrons

Oxidation – a reaction involving the gain of oxygen or the loss of hydrogen

Precipitation – the removal of particles from a solution

Proton – a positively charged particle found in the nucleus of an atom

Reduction – a reaction involving the loss of oxygen or the gain of hydrogen

Relative atomic mass (A_r) – the average mass (in atomic mass units) of the isotopes of an element

Relative formula mass (M_r) – the sum of the atomic masses of all atoms in a molecule

Reversible reaction – a reaction in which products react to reform the original reactants

Salt – the product of a chemical reaction between a base and an acid

Smart material – a material that responds to changes in its environment

Yield – the amount of a product obtained from a reaction

HT **Equilibrium** – the state in which a chemical reaction proceeds at the same rate as its reverse reaction

Unit 3

How was the periodic table developed and how can it help us understand the reactions of elements?

The periodic table classifies elements and helps us to understand the properties and reactions of the elements. To understand this, you need to know...

• about early attempts to arrange the elements in the periodic table
• how the elements are arranged in the modern periodic table
• about protons, neutrons and electrons
• about the trends within the groups.

The Periodic Table

In the modern periodic table, the elements are arranged in order of **atomic number**. They are then arranged in rows so that elements with similar properties are in the same columns, or **groups**. Arranging them in order of relative atomic mass would result in some oddities, such as argon ending up in Group 1 and potassium in Group 8, instead of the other way round.

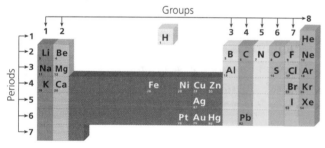

The periodic table is an arrangement of the elements in terms of their electronic structure. Elements in the same group have the same number of electrons in their outermost shell (except helium). This number also coincides with the group number. Elements in the same group have similar properties.

From left to right across each row or **period**, a particular energy level is gradually filled with electrons. In the next period, the next energy level is filled etc. (see p.12 for electronic structure).

Fewer than a quarter of the elements are non-metals. They are found in the groups to the right-hand side of the periodic table.

Early Attempts to Classify the Elements

John Newlands (1864)

Newlands only knew of the existence of 63 elements; many were still undiscovered. He arranged the known elements in order of relative atomic mass and found similar properties amongst every eighth element in the series. This makes sense since the noble gases (Group 8) weren't discovered until 1894.

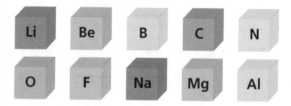

He had noticed periodicity although the missing elements caused problems.

Dimitri Mendeleev (1869)

Mendeleev realised that some elements had yet to be discovered, so he left gaps to accommodate their eventual discovery.

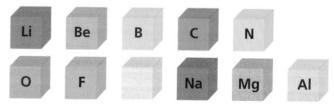

He used his periodic table to predict the existence of other elements.

Modern Chemistry

Although initially scientists regarded the periodic table as a curiosity, it later became a useful tool. The discovery of subatomic particles (protons, neutrons and electrons) and electronic structure provided a more sound base for the table since the key to similarities amongst elements is the number of electrons in the outermost energy level, i.e. Group 1 elements have 1 electron in their outermost energy level, Group 2 elements have 2 electrons and so on.

The Modern Periodic Table – Electronic Structure of the First 20 Elements

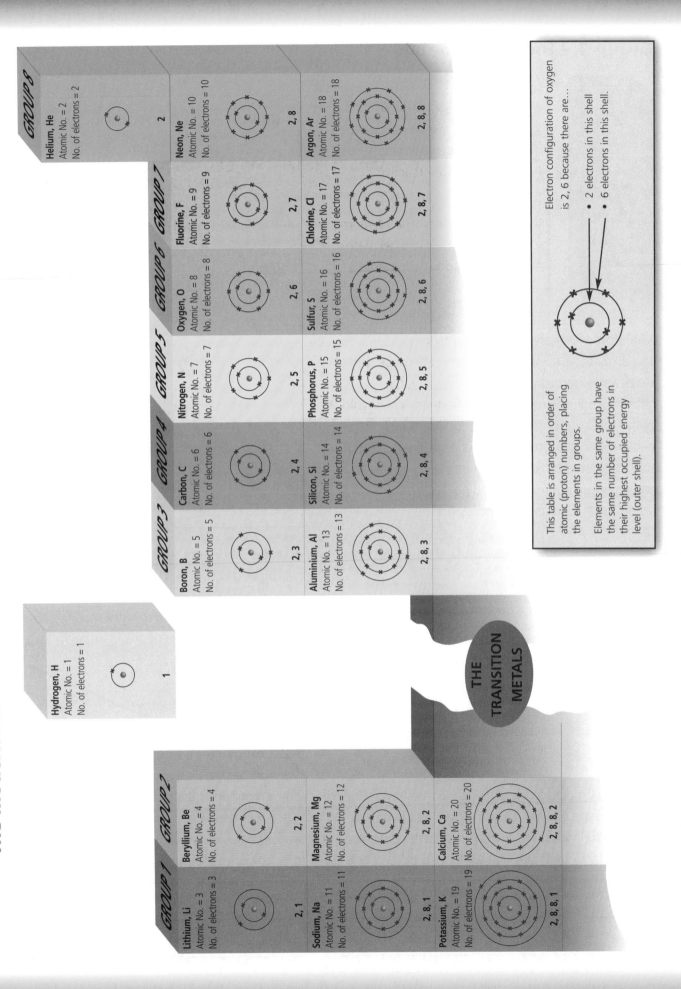

This table is arranged in order of atomic (proton) numbers, placing the elements in groups.

Elements in the same group have the same number of electrons in their highest occupied energy level (outer shell).

Electron configuration of oxygen is 2, 6 because there are...

- 2 electrons in this shell
- 6 electrons in this shell.

77

Unit 3

Group 1 – The Alkali Metals

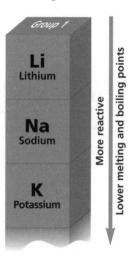

There are six metals in this group. As we go down the group, the alkali metals become more reactive.

Alkali metals have low melting points. The melting and boiling points decrease as we go down the group.

Reaction of Alkali Metals with Water

The alkali metals are stored under oil because they react very vigorously with oxygen and water. Lithium, sodium and potassium float on top of cold water (because of their low density) and melt because the heat from the reaction is great enough to turn them into liquids. Lithium reacts gently, sodium more aggressively and potassium so aggressively it melts and catches fire.

When alkali metals react with water a metal hydroxide and hydrogen gas are formed. The metal hydroxide (e.g. lithium hydroxide, sodium hydroxide) dissolves in water to form an alkaline solution, e.g....

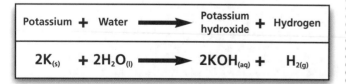

Potassium	+	Water	$\longrightarrow$	Potassium hydroxide	+	Hydrogen
$2K_{(s)}$	+	$2H_2O_{(l)}$	$\longrightarrow$	$2KOH_{(aq)}$	+	$H_{2(g)}$

Follow these steps to check the pH level of the solution formed when an alkali metal is added to water.

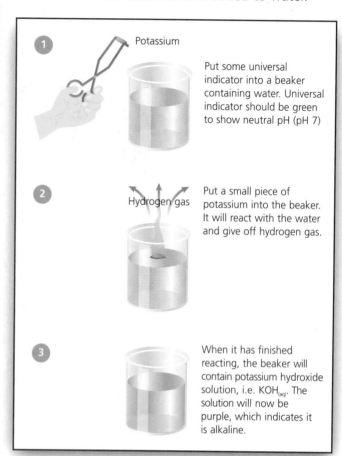

1. Put some universal indicator into a beaker containing water. Universal indicator should be green to show neutral pH (pH 7)

2. Put a small piece of potassium into the beaker. It will react with the water and give off hydrogen gas.

3. When it has finished reacting, the beaker will contain potassium hydroxide solution, i.e. $KOH_{(aq)}$. The solution will now be purple, which indicates it is alkaline.

A simple laboratory test for the production of hydrogen gas is to hold a lighted splint to the test tube of gas. If hydrogen is present, it will burn with a squeaky pop.

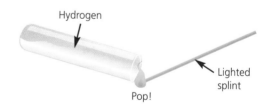

Reaction of Alkali Metals with Non-metals

When alkali metals react with non-metals to form ionic compounds the metal atom loses one electron to form a metal ion with a positive charge. The products are white solids that dissolve in water to form colourless solutions, e.g....

Sodium	+	Chlorine	$\longrightarrow$	Sodium chloride
$2Na_{(s)}$	+	$Cl_{2(s)}$	$\longrightarrow$	$2NaCl_{(aq)}$

Group 7 – The Halogens

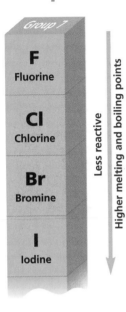

There are five non-metals in this group. As we go down the group, the melting and boiling points of halogens increase so they become less reactive.

At room temperature, fluorine and chlorine are gases and bromine is a liquid. They all have coloured vapours which, in the case of chlorine and bromine, are extremely pungent.

They exist as molecules made up of pairs of atoms.

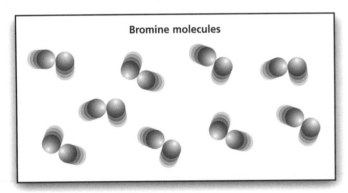

Bromine molecules

Halogens are brittle and crumbly when solid and poor conductors of heat and electricity.

Reaction of Halogens with Metals

Halogens react with metals to produce ionic salts. The halogen atom gains one electron to form a halide ion which carries a charge of -1, e.g....

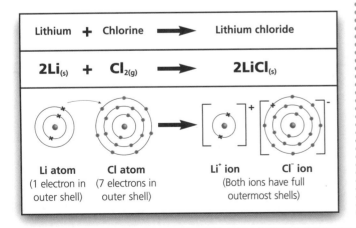

Reaction of Halogens with other Non-metallic Elements

Halogens react with other non-metallic elements to form molecular compounds.

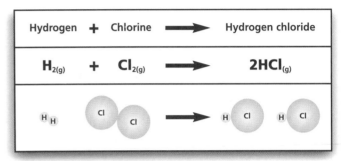

Displacement Reactions of Halogens

A more reactive halogen will displace a less reactive halogen from an aqueous solution of its salt, i.e. chlorine will displace both bromine and iodine while bromine will displace iodine.

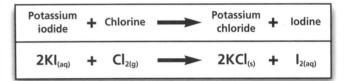

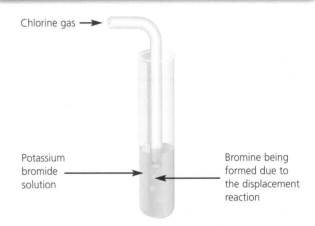

The table below shows the results of reactions between halogens and aqueous solutions of salts.

	Potassium Chloride	Potassium Bromide	Potassium Iodide
Chlorine Cl_2	X	Potassium chloride	Potassium chloride
Bromine Br_2	No reaction	X	Potassium bromide
Iodine I_2	No reaction	No reaction	X

(HT) Trends in Group 1

Alkali metals all have similar properties, because they have the same number of electrons in their outermost shell, i.e. the highest occupied energy level contains one electron.

They become more reactive as we go down the group, because the outermost electron shell gets further away from the influence of the nucleus and so an electron is more easily lost.

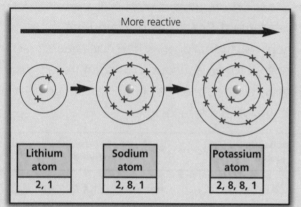

More reactive →

Lithium atom	Sodium atom	Potassium atom
2, 1	2, 8, 1	2, 8, 8, 1

Trends in Group 7

Halogens have similar properties, because they have the same number of electrons in their outermost shell, i.e. the highest occupied energy level contains seven electrons.

They become less reactive as we go down the group, because the outermost electron shell gets further away from the influence of the nucleus and so an electron is less easily gained.

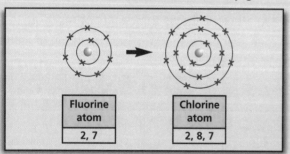

Fluorine atom	Chlorine atom
2, 7	2, 8, 7

The higher the energy level (i.e. the more shells an atom has)…
- the more easily electrons are lost
- the less easily electrons are gained.

The Transition Metals

In the centre of the periodic table, between Groups 2 and 3, is a block of metallic elements called the **transition metals**. These include iron, copper, platinum, mercury, chromium and zinc.

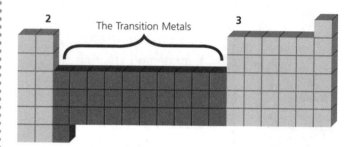

These metals…
- are hard and mechanically strong (except mercury)
- have higher densities and high melting points (except mercury, which is liquid at room temperature)
- are much less reactive than Group 1 metals and do not react as vigorously with oxygen or water
- form coloured compounds which can be used as pottery glazes, and can be seen in weathered copper which turns green.

The ions of some of the elements have different charges, e.g. Fe^{2+} and Fe^{3+}.

Many transition metals can be used as catalysts in chemical reactions. Iron and platinum are used in this way to speed up certain chemical processes.

In addition to these qualities, transition metals, like all other metals, are good conductors of heat and electricity, and can also be easily bent or hammered into shape. These properties make transition metals very useful as structural materials, and as electrical and thermal conductors.

(HT) The transition elements have similar properties and some special properties because a lower energy level (inner shell) is being filled in the atoms of the elements between Group 2 and 3. This is because the third energy level can hold up to 18 electrons once two electrons have occupied the fourth.

You need to be able to explain how attempts to classify elements in a systematic way, including those of Newlands and Mendeleev, have led through the growth of chemical knowledge to the modern periodic table and...

... explain why scientists regarded the periodic table of the elements first as a curiosity, then as a useful tool and finally as an important summary of the structure of atoms.

Scientists started to contemplate the idea of atoms 2400 years ago and there have since been many proposed theories.

As knowledge of chemical facts grew in the eighteenth and nineteenth centuries, scientists had to find patterns to avoid being overwhelmed by the mass of information and to provide the basis for understanding the facts. Previous knowledge of atomic structure helped scientists understand elements.

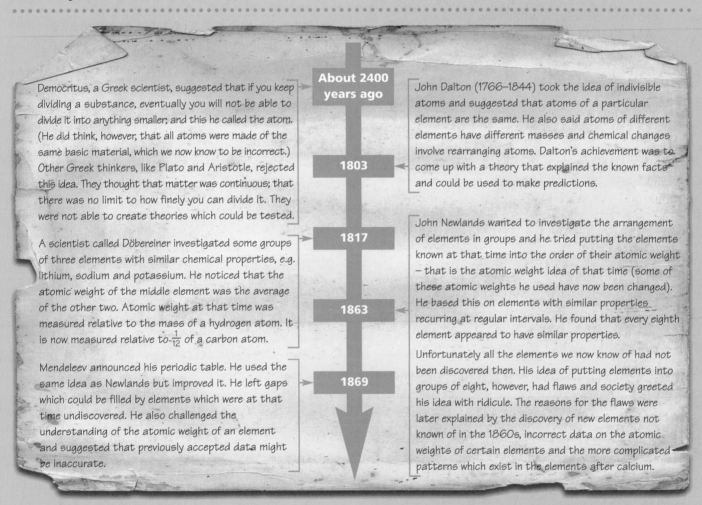

About 2400 years ago

Democritus, a Greek scientist, suggested that if you keep dividing a substance, eventually you will not be able to divide it into anything smaller, and this he called the atom. (He did think, however, that all atoms were made of the same basic material, which we now know to be incorrect.) Other Greek thinkers, like Plato and Aristotle, rejected this idea. They thought that matter was continuous; that there was no limit to how finely you can divide it. They were not able to create theories which could be tested.

1803

John Dalton (1766–1844) took the idea of indivisible atoms and suggested that atoms of a particular element are the same. He also said atoms of different elements have different masses and chemical changes involve rearranging atoms. Dalton's achievement was to come up with a theory that explained the known facts and could be used to make predictions.

1817

A scientist called Döbereiner investigated some groups of three elements with similar chemical properties, e.g. lithium, sodium and potassium. He noticed that the atomic weight of the middle element was the average of the other two. Atomic weight at that time was measured relative to the mass of a hydrogen atom. It is now measured relative to $\frac{1}{12}$ of a carbon atom.

1863

John Newlands wanted to investigate the arrangement of elements in groups and he tried putting the elements known at that time into the order of their atomic weight – that is the atomic weight idea of that time (some of these atomic weights he used have now been changed). He based this on elements with similar properties recurring at regular intervals. He found that every eighth element appeared to have similar properties.

1869

Mendeleev announced his periodic table. He used the same idea as Newlands but improved it. He left gaps which could be filled by elements which were at that time undiscovered. He also challenged the understanding of the atomic weight of an element and suggested that previously accepted data might be inaccurate.

Unfortunately all the elements we now know of had not been discovered then. His idea of putting elements into groups of eight, however, had flaws and society greeted his idea with ridicule. The reasons for the flaws were later explained by the discovery of new elements not known of in the 1860s, incorrect data on the atomic weights of certain elements and the more complicated patterns which exist in the elements after calcium.

The ideas and evidence of Mendeleev formed the basis of the modern periodic table. The elements are arranged in order of their atomic number not in order of their relative atomic mass.

Research is still taking place to try to find new elements and they are still being discovered, although many of the new elements are radioactive and exist only for a very short time. Their place in the periodic table, however, enables predictions to be made about their chemical properties.

Atomic number relates to the number of sub-atomic particles in the atom, and the number of electrons in the outer shell governs how the element reacts. Each group in the periodic table has elements in it with the same number of electrons in their outer shell. This means elements in the same group of the periodic table react in a similar way. They have similar chemical properties. It is possible to predict reactions of elements using evidence from other elements in the same group.

13.2

What are strong and weak alkalis? How can we find the amounts of acids and alkalis in solutions?

Acids and alkalis can come in different strengths and concentrations, which can be measured using titration. To understand this, you need to know...

- about acids and bases
- about hydrogen and hydroxide ions
- how titration can be used.

Acids and Alkalis

Some compounds react with water to produce acidic or alkaline solutions. On their own, these compounds sometimes do not exhibit any acidic or alkaline characteristics. For these compounds, water must be present for a substance to act as an acid or as a base.

All acids, in aqueous solution, dissociate to produce hydrogen ions (H^+). The H^+ ion is simply a proton and in water this proton is hydrated (i.e. chemically bonded to water) and is represented as $H^+_{(aq)}$. It is the presence of the $H^+_{(aq)}$ ions that gives the solution its acidic characteristics, e.g. hydrochloric acid...

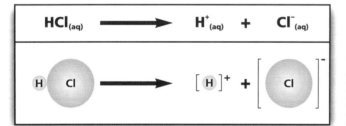

All alkalis, however, in aqueous solution, dissociate to produce OH^- (hydroxide) ions. This time the presence of the $OH^-_{(aq)}$ ions gives the solution its alkaline characteristics, e.g. sodium hydroxide...

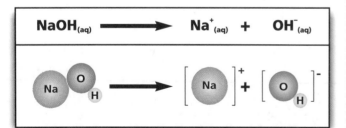

An acid can be defined as a proton donor and a base can be defined as a proton acceptor. However, an acid cannot donate a proton unless there is an appropriate base available to accept it.

Strength of Acids and Alkalis

Acids and alkalis are classified by the extent of their ionisation in water.

A strong acid or alkali is one that is completely ionised in water, i.e. all the compound dissociates into ions. Examples of strong acids are hydrochloric, sulfuric and nitric acids, while examples of strong alkalis are sodium and potassium hydroxide.

A weak acid or alkali, however, is one that is only partially ionised in water, i.e. not all of the compound dissociates into ions. Ethanoic, citric and carbonic acids are all weak acids while ammonia solution is an example of a weak alkali.

You should also be aware that you can have different acids of the same concentration which have different pH values. It simply depends on the extent of their ionisation in water. A strong concentration of an acid will therefore register a much lower pH on the pH scale than a weak concentration of the same acid.

Acids can also be distinguished by their rate of reaction with metals to produce metal salts and hydrogen. Strong acids will react more vigorously with the metal compared to a weak acid.

The concentration of an aqueous solution is usually expressed by stating how many moles of a particular solute are present in each cubic decimetre of solution. Concentration is measured in moles per cubic decimetre (mol dm^{-3} or M). One cubic decimetre is the same as 1000cm^3 or 1 litre.

Concentration of Solution	No. of Mols in 1dm³ of Solution
0.5mol dm^{-3}	0.5mol
1mol dm^{-3}	1mol
2mol dm^{-3}	2mol

Titration

Titration is an accurate technique which can be used to find out how much of an acid is needed to neutralise an alkali.

A pipette which has been carefully washed and rinsed with the alkali is used to measure out a known and accurate volume of the alkali. The alkali is then placed in a clean and dry conical flask and a suitable indicator (e.g. phenolphthalein) is added. Next, acid is placed in a burette which has been carefully washed and rinsed with the acid. An initial reading of the volume of acid in the burette is taken.

The acid is carefully added to the alkali until the indicator changes colour to show neutrality. This is called the **end point**. A final reading is taken of the volume of acid in the burette. You will then be able to calculate the volume of acid added.

The method can be repeated to check results and can then be performed without an indicator in order to obtain the salt.

You must use a suitable indicator in titrations to find the volumes of different strength acids and alkalis that react together to form a neutral solution:
- **strong acid + strong alkali** – any suitable acid-base indicator (e.g. universal, litmus).

HT
- **strong acid + weak alkali** – methyl orange indicator.
- **weak acid + strong alkali** – phenolphthalein indicator.

When neutralisation takes place, the hydrogen ions (H^+) from the acid join with the hydroxide ions (OH^-) from the alkali to form water which is neutral.

Hydrogen ion	+	Hydroxide ion	→	Water molecule
$H^+_{(aq)}$	+	$OH^-_{(aq)}$	→	$H_2O_{(l)}$

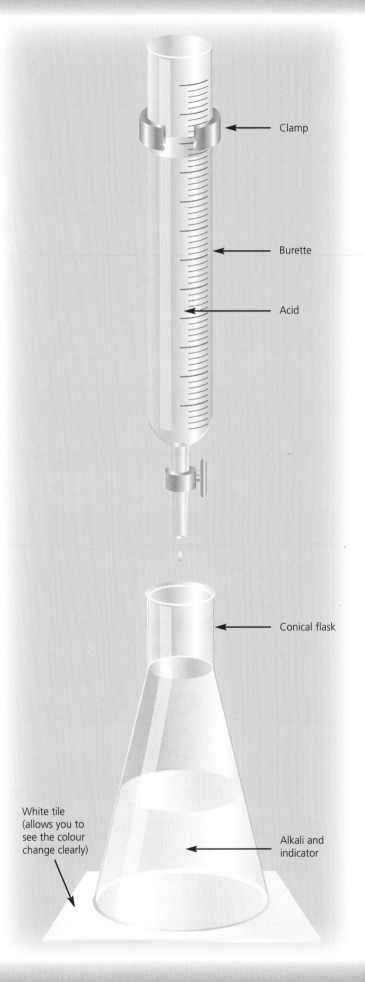

Clamp

Burette

Acid

Conical flask

White tile (allows you to see the colour change clearly)

Alkali and indicator

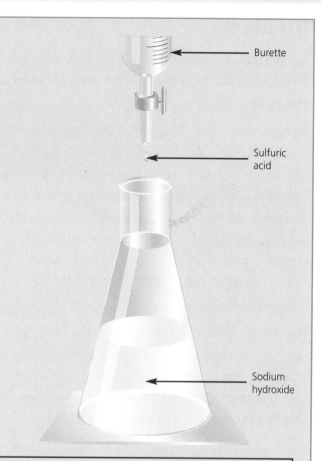

Burette

Sulfuric acid

Sodium hydroxide

Titration can be used to find the concentration of an acid or alkali providing we know either...
- the relative volumes of acid and alkali used
- the concentration of the other acid or alkali.

You will need to break down the calculation into three stages.

1 Write down a balanced equation for the reaction taking place to determine the ratio of moles of acid to alkali involved.

2 Calculate the number of moles in the solution of known volume and concentration. You will know the number of moles in the other solution from stage 1.

3 Calculate the concentration of the other solution using the formula...

$$\text{Concentration of solution (mol dm}^{-3}\text{ or M)} = \frac{\text{Number of moles of solute (mol)}}{\text{Volume of solution (dm}^3)}$$

Example 1

A titration is carried out and 0.04dm^3 of hydrochloric acid neutralises 0.08dm^3 of sodium hydroxide of concentration 1mol dm^{-3}. Calculate the concentration of the hydrochloric acid.

Write down the equation...

$$HCl_{(aq)} + NaOH_{(aq)} \longrightarrow NaCl_{(aq)} + H_2O_{(l)}$$

As you can see, 1 mole of HCl neutralises 1 mole of NaOH.

$$\text{Number of moles of NaOH (mol)} = \text{Concentration of NaOH (mol dm}^{-3}) \times \text{Volume of NaOH (dm}^3)$$

$$= 1\text{mol dm}^{-3} \times 0.08\text{dm}^3$$

$$= 0.08\text{mol}$$

Number of moles of HCl used up in the reaction is also 0.08mol.

$$\text{Concentration of HCl (mol dm}^{-3}) = \frac{\text{Number of moles of HCl (mol)}}{\text{Volume of HCl (dm}^3)}$$

$$= \frac{0.08\text{mol}}{0.04\text{dm}^3}$$

$$= 2\text{mol dm}^{-3}$$

Example 2

A titration is carried out and 0.035dm^3 of sulfuric acid of concentration 0.6mol dm^{-3} neutralises 0.14dm^3 of sodium hydroxide. Calculate the concentration of the sodium hydroxide.

Write down the equation...

$$H_2SO_{4(aq)} + 2NaOH_{(aq)} \longrightarrow Na_2SO_{4(aq)} + 2H_2O_{(l)}$$

This time, 1 mole of H_2SO_4 neutralises 2 moles of NaOH.

$$\text{Number of moles of H}_2\text{SO}_4\text{ (mol)} = \text{Concentration of H}_2\text{SO}_4\text{ (mol dm}^{-3}) \times \text{Volume of H}_2\text{SO}_4\text{ (dm}^3)$$

$$= 0.6\text{mol dm}^{-3} \times 0.035\text{dm}^3$$

$$= 0.021\text{mol}$$

Number of moles of NaOH used up in the reaction is 2 x 0.021 = 0.042mol.

$$\text{Concentration of NaOH (mol dm}^{-3}) = \frac{\text{Number of moles of NaOH (mol)}}{\text{Volume of NaOH (dm}^3)}$$

$$= \frac{0.042\text{mol}}{0.14\text{dm}^3}$$

$$= 0.3\text{mol dm}^{-3}$$

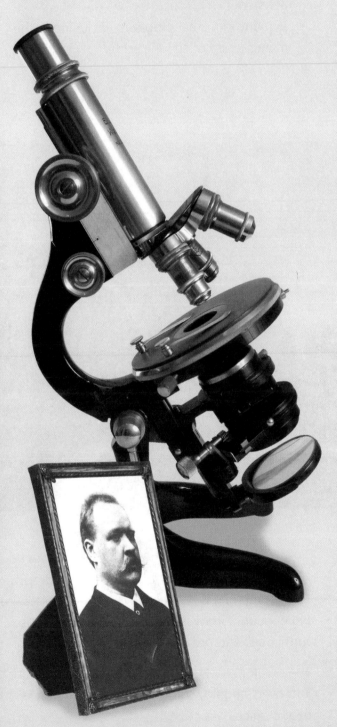

You need to be able to evaluate the contributions of Arrhenius, Lowry and Brønsted to our understanding of acid–base behaviour and suggest why the work of some scientists, for example Arrhenius, took much longer to be accepted than the work of others, for example, Lowry and Brønsted.

In 1887 Arrhenius (a Swedish chemist, pictured below) proposed that…

- all acids release hydrogen ions when they are dissolved in water
- alkalis (soluble bases) form hydroxide ions in water
- molecules ionise in water.

This idea is very restricted and only applies to acids and bases which dissolve in water; it does not take into account gases. For example, ammonia gas can react as a base, and hydrogen chloride gas is an acid even when it is not dissolved in water.

In 1923, Lowry (an English chemist) and Brønsted (a Danish chemist) proposed that…

- acids are proton donors
- bases are proton acceptors
- an acid cannot donate a proton unless there is an appropriate base available to accept it.

These ideas work for soluble and insoluble bases and also hold true for the reaction of gases.

Arrhenius's work took longer to be accepted because at the time when he was working (1880s) subatomic charged particles (protons, neutrons and electrons) had not been discovered. His ideas were radically different from anything that had previously been proposed, so people found his ideas hard to understand. Also, his theory did not accept the reaction of gases as being acid–base, because it did not involve hydrogen and hydroxide ions in solution in water.

People were much more accepting of Lowry's and Brønsted's ideas because they were able to explain the behaviour of acids and bases in solvents other than water.

Also, Lowry and Brønsted worked independently and their ideas supported each other.

Unit 3

13.3

What is in the water we drink?

Although water contains dissolved substances, it should be safe to drink. To understand this, you need to know…

- how the water cycle works
- what factors affect how substances dissolve in water
- that some gases dissolve in water
- properties of hard and soft water
- how to produce pure water.

The Importance of Water

Water is the most abundant substance on the surface of the Earth and it is essential for the existence of all life. It is an important raw material and has many uses, including…

- as a solvent where substances are dissolved in it
- as a coolant for the removal of heat from a system
- in many industrial processes (including in the manufacture of sulfuric acid).

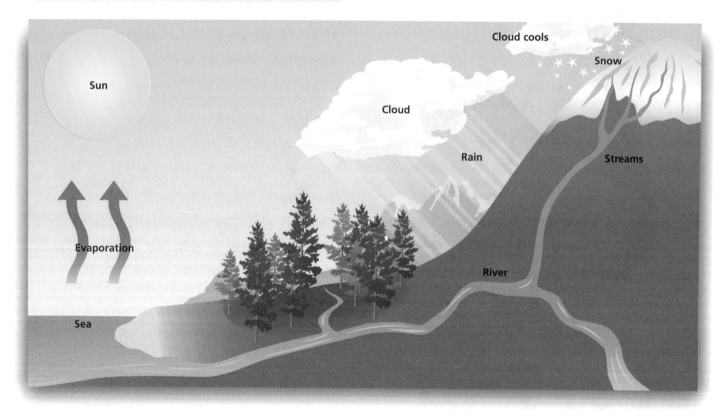

The Water Cycle

The diagram above shows the water cycle.

The Sun provides the energy, which drives the water cycle. Heat energy from the Sun causes water in rivers, lakes and oceans to rise via evaporation.

As the water vapour rises higher and higher into the atmosphere, it cools and condensation occurs forming droplets of water which collect together to form clouds.

As the clouds rise higher the temperature drops further and rain is produced when the droplets are big enough. (Snow is produced when clouds rise further still and get even colder.)

The rain (or snow) then falls onto the land, drains into rivers and flows into the sea, and the cycle begins again.

Drinking Water

In order to produce water which is good quality and safe to drink, the water is passed through a filter bed to remove any solid particles. Chlorine gas is then added to kill any harmful microorganisms.

It is also essential to ensure that the levels of dissolved salts are sufficiently low. More dissolved substances can be removed from tap water to improve the quality by passing the water through a filter containing carbon, silver and ion exchange resins.

Any water can be distilled to produce **pure water** which has no dissolved substances in it. This process involves boiling water to produce steam and condensing the steam by cooling it to produce pure liquid water. This process uses a great deal of energy, which makes it expensive.

Dissolving Substances in Water

If a solid dissolves in water it is said to be **soluble**. The solid which dissolves is called the **solute** and water is described as the **solvent**. Water is sometimes called the universal solvent as so many substances dissolve in it.

Solubility of Compounds

In general, most ionic compounds, e.g. sodium chloride and copper sulfate, are soluble in water. Most covalent compounds, e.g. silicon dioxide, are insoluble in water, although some molecular substances are soluble.

The solubility of a solute in water (or another solvent) is usually given in grams of solute per 100 grams of water (g/100g of water) at that temperature. The temperature of the solvent plays an important part and the solubility of most solutes increases as the temperature increases. This can be shown using a solubility curve. A typical solubility curve for copper sulfate in water is shown opposite.

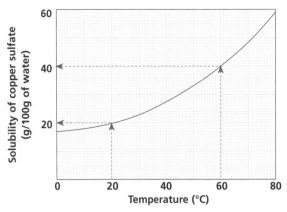

Any point on the curve tells us the maximum amount of copper sulfate that dissolves at a particular temperature in 100g of water to give us a **saturated solution**. We can use the graph to find out how many grams of copper sulfate per 100g of water is needed to make a saturated solution…

- at 20°C it is 20g/100g of water
- at 60°C it is 40g/100g of water.

When a warm saturated solution of copper sulfate cools down, some of the copper sulfate will separate from the solution and crystallisation occurs, e.g. if the solution is cooled down from 60°C to 20°C then 20g (40g – 20g) of copper sulfate per 100g of water will crystallise out.

Solubility of Gases

Many gases are soluble in water. The solubility of these gases increases as the temperature of the water decreases or as the pressure on the water increases. Two gases that are soluble are…

1. **carbon dioxide** – dissolving carbon dioxide under high pressure produces carbonated water, which is used in fizzy drinks such as lemonade. Unscrewing the bottle top releases the pressure and results in carbon dioxide bubbling out of the solution. Also, keeping drinks in the fridge increases the solubility of CO_2 and keeps them fizzy.

2. **oxygen** – oxygen dissolves in water and this dissolved oxygen is essential for aquatic life. However, the discharge of hot water from power stations reduces the amount of oxygen dissolved in the water. This lack of oxygen can damage aquatic life.

Unit 3

Hard and Soft Water

Water is a solvent and many compounds can dissolve in it. The amount of these compounds present determines whether the tap water is described as **hard** or **soft**.

Most hard water contains calcium or magnesium compounds which dissolve in natural water that flows over ground or rocks containing compounds of these elements. These dissolved substances react with soap to form scum, which makes it harder to form a lather.

Soft water does not contain many dissolved compounds so it readily forms a lather with soap.

The advantages and disadvantages of hard water are:

Advantages	Disadvantages
• The dissolved compounds in water are good for your health, e.g. calcium compounds help in the development of strong bones and teeth. They also help to reduce the development of heart diseases.	• More soap is needed to form a lather, which increases costs. • It often leads to deposits (called scale) forming in heating systems and appliances like kettles. This reduces their efficiency.

Removing Hardness

To make hard water soft, we have to remove the dissolved calcium and magnesium ions contained in it. To do this we can…

• add sodium carbonate solution (washing soda) to it. The carbonate ions react with the calcium and magnesium ions to form calcium carbonate and magnesium carbonate respectively which precipitate out of solution as they are both insoluble. For example…

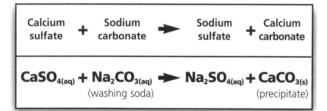

| Calcium sulfate | + | Sodium carbonate | ➡ | Sodium sulfate | + | Calcium carbonate |

$$CaSO_{4(aq)} + Na_2CO_{3(aq)} \rightarrow Na_2SO_{4(aq)} + CaCO_{3(s)}$$

(washing soda)   (precipitate)

• pass the hard water through an ion-exchange column (see opposite). The column contains a special resin which supplies hydrogen ions, $H^+_{(aq)}$ or sodium ions, $Na^+_{(aq)}$. As the hard water passes through the resin, the calcium and magnesium ions contained in it are replaced by hydrogen or sodium ions from the resin. The calcium and magnesium ions consequently remain in the resin. The resin has to be replaced when it 'runs out' of hydrogen or sodium ions.

Ion-exchange column

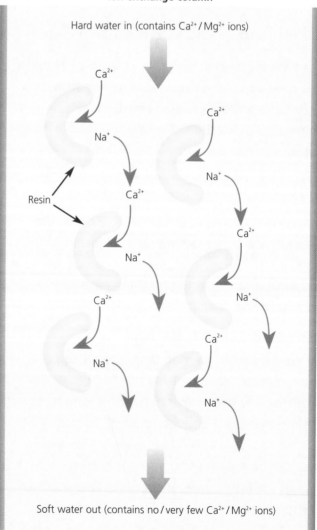

Hard water in (contains Ca^{2+} / Mg^{2+} ions)

Resin

Soft water out (contains no / very few Ca^{2+} / Mg^{2+} ions)

You need to be able to consider and evaluate the environmental, social and economic aspects of water quality and hardness.

Example

waterwatch

When is pure not pure?

Water is the most abundant substance on the Earth's surface and it is important that water is fit to drink as polluted water can cause illnesses. The water we drink cannot be described as pure because it contains dissolved minerals it has collected on its way under and over the ground to the reservoir where it is stored. The World Health Organisation (WHO), The Environment Agency and Water Quality Association all employ people who carefully monitor what happens to our drinking water. Many human activities and their by-products have the potential to pollute water. Large and small industrial enterprises, agriculture, horticulture, transport, animals and humans can all bring about water pollution.

Water scare over

Two months ago, there was an outbreak of cryptosporidium, a stomach illness that can be caught by drinking infected water. In Anglesey and Gwynedd, there were 231 reported cases of people catching the bug. As a result, everyone in the North Wales area has had to boil their water before consuming it to remove the risk of getting infected.

The infected water is likely to have come from the Llyn Cwellyn reservoir, but health officials have now given North Wales' residents the all clear; there is no need to continue boiling their water.

However, what remains to be seen is the impact of this scare. General consensus is that people are still wary of their water, and some say they've switched to drinking only bottled water.

What's in our bottles?

There are plenty of brands of bottled water on the market – still, sparkling and even flavoured water – and the demand for them does not seem to be slowing down. When the average cost of a household's daily water usage is 68p, why are so many people happy to spend more than that on half a litre of bottled water?

There are many reasons why people choose to pay more to drink bottled water rather than drink the much cheaper alternative that comes out of their taps. Many people cite the fresher taste as their main reason for drinking bottled water. This fresher taste is because bottled water does not contain chlorine, which is used in the treatment of tap water. Interestingly, the drinking water inspectorate has claimed that most people cannot tell the difference between a glass of chilled tap water and a glass of chilled bottled water.

Others say they only buy bottled water as a convenience when they are out and about, and they choose water

because it is a healthier alternative to the fizzy and sugary drinks on sale. However, many people claim they buy bottled water when they are out for the day, rather than taking a bottle of their own tap water, because it is chilled, which makes it more refreshing.

Another contributing factor is health fears, such as the contamination of tap water supplies. Bottled water companies latch on to this fear and use words such as 'clear', 'pure' and 'natural' to reinforce the idea that their water is clean and good for you. A leading foundation has recently stated that most worries about tap water have been exaggerated and that there is no reason why people should choose bottled water over tap water as far as their health is concerned.

However, even with the ever-increasing trend towards consuming bottled water rather than tap water, we still have a long way to go to catch up with the continent. In France, Germany and Italy, 90% of adults drink bottled water.

Unit 3

13.4

How much energy is involved in chemical reactions?

The energy involved in a chemical reaction can be measured. We need to control the amount of energy we consume to avoid obesity. To understand this, you need to know…

- how to measure the amount of energy released when substances burn
- why energy is required in a chemical reaction
- about exothermic and endothermic reactions.

Joules and Calories

When any chemical change takes place it is accompanied by an energy change. If heat energy is given out it is an **exothermic reaction**, when it is taken in it is an **endothermic reaction** (see p.63).

The unit of measurement for energy is the **joule** (**J**). It takes 4.2 joules of energy to heat up 1g of water by 1°C. This amount of energy is called **1 calorie**.

Information about ingredients on food products show how much energy can be provided by 100g of that particular food (see opposite). This information is often given in kilocalories (1000 calories).

Eating and digesting food brings about an energy change in our bodies. Different foods produce different amounts of energy. Large amounts of energy are provided by fats and oils. Carbohydrates also produce energy, but proteins produce less energy.

If we eat too much food and take too little exercise, the excess energy is stored in our bodies in the form of fat. If you continue to store fat in this way, you can become very overweight and are described as being **obese**. Obesity could lead to other illnesses such as heart disease and diabetes.

Obese Person

Nutritional Value of a Packet of Crisps

CRISPS
READY SALTED

NUTRITION INFORMATION

Typical Values Per 100g
Energy	2234kJ
Protein	5.9g
Carbohydrates	54.6g
Fat	35.0g
Fibre	5.4g
Sodium	0.6g

Nutritional Value of a Tin of Tomato Soup

NUTRITION INFORMATION

Typical Values	Per 100g
Energy	182kJ
Protein	0.8g
Carbohydrates	6.0g
Fat	1.8g
Fibre	0.6g
Sodium	0.3g

Measuring Energy

The method of measuring the relative amounts of heat energy released by burning a substance is called **calorimetry** as the equipment used is called a calorimeter. Calorimeters are usually made from metal or glass.

To measure the temperature change that takes place when a fuel burns you need to…

1. place 100g of water in a calorimeter and take the temperature of the water
2. find the mass (in grams) of the fuel to be burnt
3. burn the fuel under the water in the calorimeter for a few minutes and record the temperature change of the water
4. weigh the fuel again to calculate how much fuel has been used.

The amount of energy produced in a chemical reaction in solution can be measured by mixing the reactants in an insulated container, which enables the temperature change to be measured before heat is lost to the surroundings. This method would be suitable for neutralisation reactions and the reaction of solids and water.

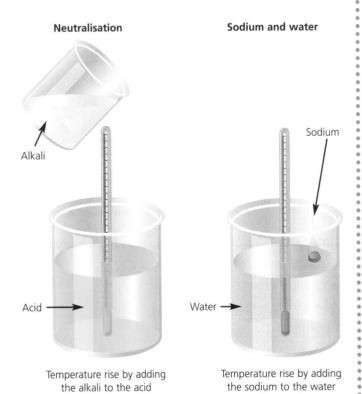

Neutralisation

Alkali

Acid

Temperature rise by adding the alkali to the acid

Sodium and water

Sodium

Water

Temperature rise by adding the sodium to the water

Example

Calculate the energy per gram produced by burning methylated spirits (meths.).

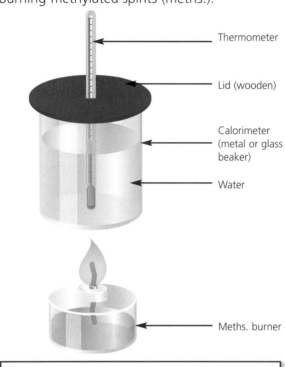

Thermometer

Lid (wooden)

Calorimeter (metal or glass beaker)

Water

Meths. burner

Temperature change	=	Highest temperature reached	−	Temperature at start

	Before	After	Difference
Mass of meths. and burner	125g	122.6g	125 − 122.6 = 2.4g
Temperature of 100g of water	21°C	37°C	37 − 21 = 16°C

So, 2.4g of meths. raises 100g of water by 16°C.

We know that 4.2 joules of energy will raise the temperature of 1g of water by 1°C, so we can use this to calculate how many joules it will take to heat 100g of water…

4.2 x 100 x 16 = 6720 joules

So, now we know that 2.4g of meths. produces 6720 joules of energy, we can work out how much energy 1g of meths. will produce…

$$\frac{6720}{2.4} = 2800J = \textbf{2.8kJ/g}$$

Unit 3

Making and Breaking Bonds

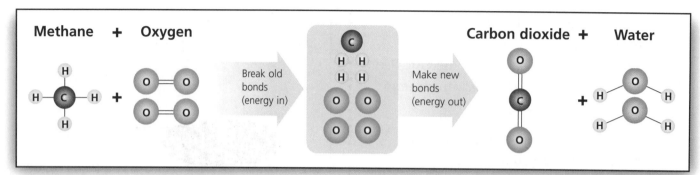

In a chemical reaction, new substances are produced. In order to do this, the bonds in the reactants must be broken and new bonds made to form the products.

Breaking a chemical bond requires a lot of energy – this must be an **endothermic** process.

When a new chemical bond is formed, energy is given out – this must be an **exothermic** process.

We can use this idea to find out if a chemical reaction is exothermic or endothermic overall (see below).

Endothermic

If more energy is required to break old bonds than is released when the new bonds are formed, the reaction must be **endothermic**.

Exothermic

If more energy is released when the new bonds are formed than is needed to break the old bonds, the reaction must be **exothermic**.

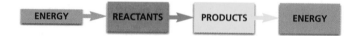

Energy Level Diagrams

The energy changes in a chemical reaction can be illustrated using an energy level diagram.

Exothermic Processes

In an exothermic reaction energy is given out. This means energy is being lost so the products have less energy than the reactants.

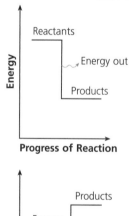

Endothermic Processes

In an endothermic reaction, energy is being taken in. This means that energy is being gained, so the products have more energy than the reactants.

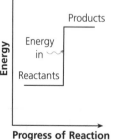

Activation Energy

The activation energy is the energy needed to start a reaction, i.e. to break the old bonds. We can show this on an energy level diagram too.

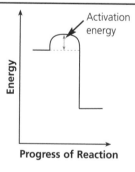

Catalysts

Catalysts reduce the activation energy needed for a reaction – this makes the reaction go faster.

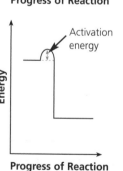

You need to be able to compare the energy produced by different fuels and foods and...

... consider the social, economic and environmental consequences of using fuels.

Example

F A C T S H E E T

Most fossil-fuelled power stations burn coal or natural gas. The main products from burning coal in a power station are carbon dioxide (CO_2) and smoke. The increase of carbon dioxide levels in the atmosphere is believed to be responsible for the Greenhouse Effect which could result in global warming. Smoke contains microscopic particles of carbon, called particulates. Although they are small, they are much bigger than atoms and molecules and each particle contains billions of carbon atoms. It is claimed that they can make asthma and lung infections worse.

Over the last two and a half years, Drax Power Station has been developing the use of biomass as a fuel to use in addition to coal in order to try to reduce emissions of carbon dioxide.

Biomass has replaced 2.5% of coal at Drax and this has reduced emissions of carbon dioxide by around 0.5 million tonnes a year. Further modifications at Drax could save a remarkable 4.4 million tonnes a year.

The National Farmers' Union (NFU) president has said that British farmers have a vested interest in reducing the impact of climate change.

Out of all energy crops, willow represents the least intensive crop. It can be grown and harvested every 3 years to produce wood chip, and a willow plantation can remain viable for up to 20 years.

Fuel	Advantages	Disadvantages
Biomass (e.g. willow)	• Less CO_2 emissions. • Renewable energy source, so it is sustainable. • Burning wood does not contribute as much to global warming as burning fossil fuels.	• Produces SO_2 which produces acid rain. • Large area needed to grow trees that could be used for another purpose. • Not very efficient if small plants are used. • Not as much energy (heat) produced as there is from coal.
Fossil fuel (e.g. coal, gas)	• Large amounts of energy can be produced, very cheaply. • Gas power stations are very efficient.	• Non-renewable energy source (will run out). • Produces CO_2 which contributes to the Greenhouse Effect. • Produces SO_2 which produces acid rain. • Produces particulates and pollution. • Adverse effects on health, particularly for asthma sufferers.

How Science Works

You need to be able to calculate the energy transferred in reactions, using simple energy level diagrams or supplied bond energies.

Supplied Bond Energies

We can find out whether a reaction is exothermic or endothermic by calculating the difference between the energy used to make bonds and the energy used to break bonds. For example, when methane burns, the products formed are carbon dioxide and water. The reaction can be represented by the equation below:

Methane + Oxygen ⟶	Carbon dioxide	+ Water
$CH_{4(g)}$ + $2O_{2(g)}$ ⟶	$CO_{2(g)}$	+ $2H_2O_{(l)}$

Bond energies for the reactants and products are...

    C–H is 412kJ
    O=O is 496kJ
    C=O is 805kJ
    H–O is 463kJ

Energy used to break bonds is...

    4 C–H = 4 x 412 = 1648kJ
    2 O=O = 992kJ
    Total = 1648kJ + 992kJ = **2640kJ**

Energy used to make bonds is...

    2 C=O = 2 x 805 = 1610kJ
    4 H–O = 4 x 463 = 1852kJ
    Total = 1610kJ + 1852kJ = **3462kJ**

Energy change (ΔH) = Energy used to break bonds – Energy used to make bonds

    = 2640kJ – 3462kJ = **-822kJ**

The reaction is exothermic (energy is given out) because the energy for making the bonds in the products is more than the energy needed for breaking the bonds in the reactants.

Simple Energy Level Diagrams

Hydrogen and oxygen are burnt to produce water.

Hydrogen + Oxygen ⟶	Water
$2H_{2(g)}$ + $O_{2(g)}$ ⟶	$2H_2O_{(aq)}$

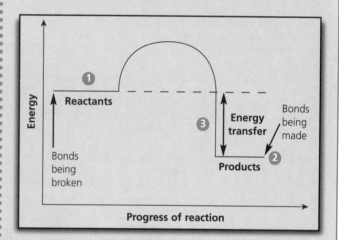

Bond energies for the reactants and products are...

    H–H is 436
    O=O is 496
    H–O is 463

Energy used to break bonds is...

    $2H_2 + O_2$
    = (2 x 436) + 496
    = **1368kJ**

Energy used to make bonds is...

    $2H_2O$
    2 x (2 x 463)
    = **1852kJ**

Energy change (ΔH) = Energy used to break bonds – Energy used to make bonds

    = 1368kJ – 1852kJ = **-484kJ**

The reaction is exothermic.

Unit 3

13.5

How do we identify and analyse substances?

Chemical tests can identify elements and compounds, even in small samples. To understand this, you need to know…

- about flame tests
- how carbonates react
- what happens to ions in solutions
- what happens to organic compounds when heated
- what instruments are used, and why.

A range of chemical tests can be carried out to detect and identify elements and compounds.

Flame Tests

Lithium, sodium, potassium, calcium, barium and copper compounds can be recognised by the distinctive colours they produce in a flame test.

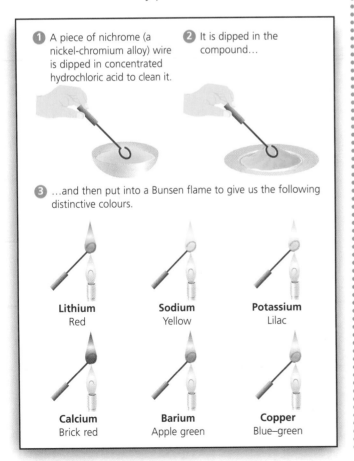

1. A piece of nichrome (a nickel-chromium alloy) wire is dipped in concentrated hydrochloric acid to clean it.

2. It is dipped in the compound…

3. …and then put into a Bunsen flame to give us the following distinctive colours.

Lithium Red
Sodium Yellow
Potassium Lilac
Calcium Brick red
Barium Apple green
Copper Blue–green

Reaction of Carbonates with Dilute Acid

Carbonates react with dilute acids to form carbon dioxide gas (and a salt and water). For example, if we add calcium carbonate to dilute hydrochloric acid then the carbonate will 'fizz' as it reacts with the acid, giving off carbon dioxide.

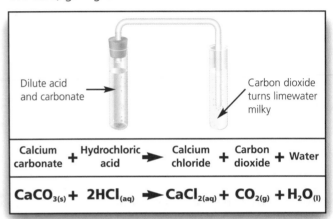

Dilute acid and carbonate

Carbon dioxide turns limewater milky

| Calcium carbonate | + | Hydrochloric acid | → | Calcium chloride | + | Carbon dioxide | + | Water |

$$CaCO_{3(s)} + 2HCl_{(aq)} \rightarrow CaCl_{2(aq)} + CO_{2(g)} + H_2O_{(l)}$$

Thermal Decomposition of Copper and Zinc Carbonate

When copper carbonate and zinc carbonate are heated, a thermal decomposition reaction takes place. This results in a distinctive colour change which enables the two compounds to be identified.

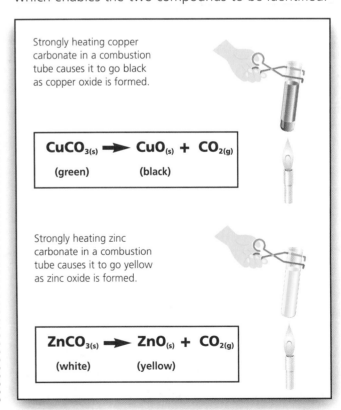

Strongly heating copper carbonate in a combustion tube causes it to go black as copper oxide is formed.

$$CuCO_{3(s)} \rightarrow CuO_{(s)} + CO_{2(g)}$$
(green) (black)

Strongly heating zinc carbonate in a combustion tube causes it to go yellow as zinc oxide is formed.

$$ZnCO_{3(s)} \rightarrow ZnO_{(s)} + CO_{2(g)}$$
(white) (yellow)

Unit 3

Metal Ions

Metal compounds in solution contain metal ions. Some of these form precipitates, i.e. insoluble solids that come out of solution when sodium hydroxide solution is added to them. In the example opposite, a white precipitate of calcium hydroxide is formed (as well as sodium chloride solution). We can see how this precipitate is formed by considering the ions involved.

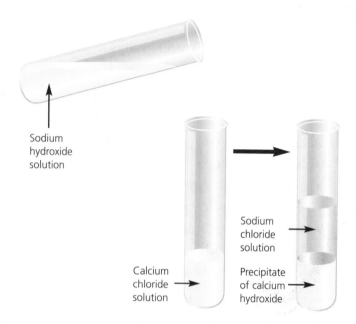

$Ca^{2+}_{(aq)}$	+	$2OH^-_{(aq)}$	$\longrightarrow$	$Ca(OH)_{2(s)}$
from the calcium chloride		from the sodium hydroxide		

The table below shows the colour of precipitate formed when certain metal ions are mixed with sodium hydroxide solution. Only the aluminium hydroxide precipitate dissolves in excess sodium hydroxide solution.

Metal Ion + Sodium Hydroxide	Precipitate Formed	Colour of Precipitate
Aluminium $Al^{3+}_{(aq)}$ + Sodium hydroxide	Aluminium hydroxide	White
Calcium $Ca^{2+}_{(aq)}$ + Sodium hydroxide	Calcium hydroxide	White
Magnesium $Mg^{2+}_{(aq)}$ + Sodium hydroxide	Magnesium hydroxide	White
Copper $Cu^{2+}_{(aq)}$ + Sodium hydroxide	Copper hydroxide	Blue
Iron $Fe^{2+}_{(aq)}$ + Sodium hydroxide	Iron hydroxide	Green
Iron $Fe^{3+}_{(aq)}$ + Sodium hydroxide	Iron hydroxide	Brown

Sulfate Ions – To identify the presence of a sulfate ion, add barium chloride solution and dilute hydrochloric acid to the suspected sulfate solution. A white precipitate of barium sulfate will be produced if a sulfate is present (see ❶ opposite).

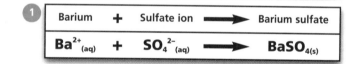

Nitrate Ions – To identify the presence of a nitrate ion, add aluminium powder and sodium hydroxide solution to the suspected nitrate. If a nitrate is present the nitrate ions are reduced to form ammonia (which can be identified as it turns damp litmus paper blue).

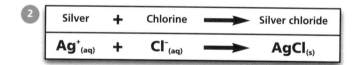

Chloride, Bromide and Iodide Ions – To identify the presence of a chloride, bromide or iodide ion, add silver nitrate solution and nitric acid to the suspected halide solution. A white precipitate will form if silver chloride is present, a cream precipitate for silver bromide, and a yellow precipitate for silver iodide (see ❷, ❸, ❹ opposite).

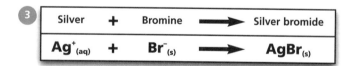

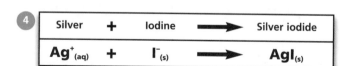

Tests for Organic Compounds

The gas in a Bunsen burner or gas fire burns with a blue flame when it has a plentiful supply of oxygen. This is called **complete combustion**. The carbon in the gas is oxidised to carbon dioxide and the hydrogen is oxidised to water, e.g. the complete combustion of methane, CH_4...

Complete combustion

Methane	+	Oxygen	⟶	Carbon dioxide	+	Water
$CH_{4(g)}$	+	$O_{2(g)}$	⟶	$CO_{2(g)}$	+	$2H_2O_{(l)}$

However, the gas in a Bunsen burner burns with a yellow / orange flame if it has a limited supply of air. The flame is then smoky and produces lots of soot or carbon particles. The greater the proportion of carbon in the organic compound the more yellow and smoky the flame. This is called **incomplete combustion** and instead of carbon dioxide, carbon monoxide is produced.

Incomplete combustion

Methane	+	Oxygen	⟶	Carbon monoxide	+	Water
$2CH_{4(g)}$	+	$3O_{2(g)}$	⟶	$2CO_{(g)}$	+	$4H_2O_{(l)}$

Carbon monoxide is a toxic, colourless and odourless gas which combines irreversibly with the haemoglobin in red blood cells reducing its oxygen-carrying capacity. This eventually results in death through a lack of oxygen reaching cells. However, if there is *very* little oxygen available, carbon is produced instead...

Carbon is made

Methane	+	Oxygen	⟶	Carbon	+	Water
$CH_{4(g)}$	+	$O_{2(g)}$	⟶	$C_{(s)}$	+	$2H_2O_{(l)}$

The surfaces of solid organic compounds will blacken or char if they are burnt in air. Black marks can be seen on the surface of organic compounds which are burnt as **carbon** is made.

Bromine water can be used to identify an unsaturated organic compound that contains double carbon carbon bonds. If bromine water is shaken with an unsaturated organic compound the bromine water would change from brown to colourless. Bromine water would stay brown if shaken with a saturated organic compound. (This is because it cannot form a bond with a saturated compound).

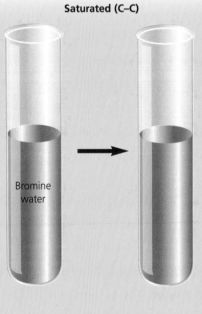

Saturated (C–C)

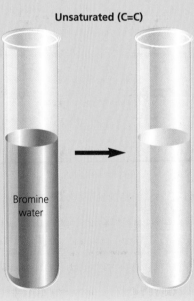

Unsaturated (C=C)

Empirical Formulae

The **empirical formula** of a compound shows the ratio of all the elements in that compound.

It is possible to calculate the empirical formula of an organic compound by burning a known mass of the compound in oxygen and measuring the masses of all the products.

Example 1

11g of carbon dioxide and 9g of water are produced when 4g of an organic compound is burnt completely in oxygen. What is the empirical formula of the compound?

Find the mass of each element in the products, except for oxygen (which did not come from the organic compound).

M_r of water, H_2O = (2 x 1) + 16 = 18
So, water is $\frac{2}{18}$ hydrogen and $\frac{16}{18}$ oxygen. Therefore, mass of hydrogen in 9g of water = $\frac{2}{18}$ x 9g = **1g**

M_r of carbon dioxide, CO_2 = 12 + (2 x 16) = 44 So, carbon dioxide is $\frac{12}{44}$ carbon and $\frac{32}{44}$ oxygen. The mass of carbon in 11g of carbon dioxide = $\frac{12}{44}$ x 11g = **3g**

Now, divide each mass by the element's atomic mass...

H = 1 ∴ Hydrogen = $\frac{1}{1}$ = 1 mole
C = 12 ∴ Carbon = $\frac{3}{12}$ = 0.25 mole

Find the ratio of one element to the other...

Ratio of hydrogen to carbon is 1 : 0.25 = 4 : 1

There are 4 atoms of hydrogen to 1 atom of carbon.

The empirical formula of the original organic compound is CH_4.

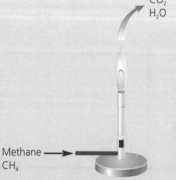

Methane
CH_4

Example 2

4.4g of an organic hydrocarbon was burned in oxygen producing 13.2g of carbon dioxide and 7.2g of water. What is the empirical formula of the hydrocarbon?

Find the mass of each element in the products, except for oxygen (which did not come from the organic compound).

Mass of hydrogen in 7.2g of water
= $\frac{2}{18}$ x 7.2g = **0.8g**

Mass of carbon in 13.2g of carbon dioxide
= $\frac{12}{44}$ x 13.2g = **3.6g**

Now, divide each mass by the element's atomic mass...

H = 1 ∴ Hydrogen = $\frac{0.8}{1}$ = 0.8 mole
C = 12 ∴ Carbon = $\frac{3.6}{12}$ = 0.3 mole

Find the ratio of one element to the other...

Ratio of carbon to hydrogen is 0.3 : 0.8 = 3 : 8

There are 8 atoms of hydrogen to 3 atoms of carbon.

The empirical formula of the original organic hydrocarbon is C_3H_8.

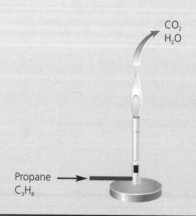

Propane
C_3H_8

Instrumental Methods

Standard laboratory equipment can be used to detect and identify elements and compounds. However, instrumental methods that involve using highly accurate instruments to analyse and identify substances have been developed to perform this function. The table below shows some of the advantages and disadvantages of using instruments to identify elements and compounds:

Advantages	Disadvantages
• Rapid results. • Very sensitive and accurate. • Small samples can be used. • Easily automated and computerised. • Staff do not need to be as highly trained to interpret the results.	• Machines are expensive to buy, run and maintain. • The sample must be completely pure because even the tiniest traces of other substances can be detected. • All the settings of the machine must be checked meticulously before use (using standard samples of purity) to ensure accurate results are obtained.

Industrial Applications

Some instrumental methods are used to identify elements, such as atomic absorption spectroscopy, which is used in the steel industry.

Other instrumental methods are used to identify compounds. These methods include…
• infra red spectrometry
• ultraviolet spectroscopy
• nuclear magnetic resonance spectroscopy
• gas–liquid chromatography.

Mass spectrometry measures the deflection of ions of the substance as they pass through the magnetic field of the spectrometer. It can be used to identify elements or compounds.

Rapid progress in electronics and computing have provided the basis for the development of accurate instrumental methods of analysing substances.

In addition, there is now greater interest in the quick and effective monitoring of changes in environmental conditions. At its simplest, this can be seen easily enough in emission-detecting equipment in garages.

Developments in fibre optics and magnetometry have also made equipment more sophisticated. Advances in technology have led to…
• increased miniaturisation
• greater sensitivity
• ease of use
• greater automation
• greater versatility.

Example Questions

For Unit 3, you will have to complete one written
paper with structured questions.

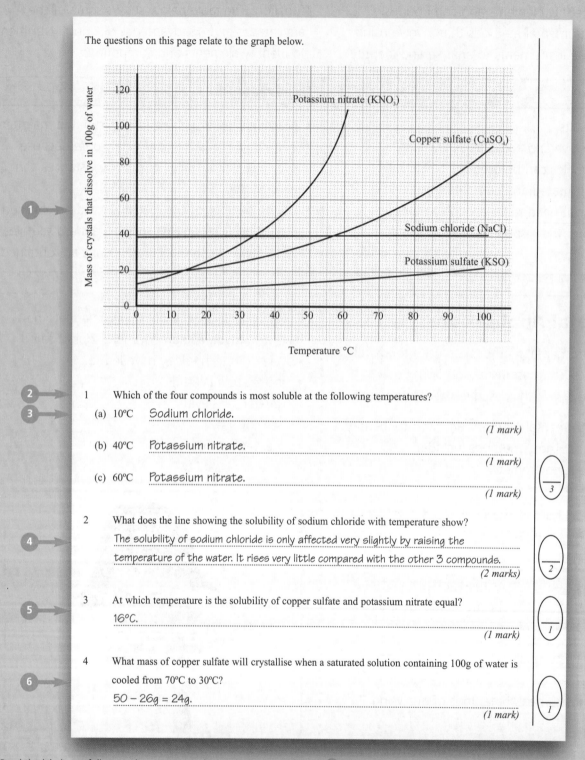

The questions on this page relate to the graph below.

Mass of crystals that dissolve in 100g of water

Potassium nitrate (KNO₃)

Copper sulfate (CuSO₄)

Sodium chloride (NaCl)

Potassium sulfate (KSO)

Temperature °C

1   Which of the four compounds is most soluble at the following temperatures?

   (a) 10°C   <u>Sodium chloride.</u>

(1 mark)

   (b) 40°C   <u>Potassium nitrate.</u>

(1 mark)

   (c) 60°C   <u>Potassium nitrate.</u>

(1 mark)

(3)

2   What does the line showing the solubility of sodium chloride with temperature show?

<u>The solubility of sodium chloride is only affected very slightly by raising the</u>
<u>temperature of the water. It rises very little compared with the other 3 compounds.</u>

(2 marks)

(2)

3   At which temperature is the solubility of copper sulfate and potassium nitrate equal?

<u>16°C.</u>

(1 mark)

(1)

4   What mass of copper sulfate will crystallise when a saturated solution containing 100g of water is
cooled from 70°C to 30°C?

<u>50 – 26g = 24g.</u>

(1 mark)

(1)

① Read the labels carefully to make sure you understand what a graph
or diagram shows before answering any questions.
② Questions like this test your skills at reading and interpreting data.
Take your time, to avoid making silly mistakes.
③ The greater the mass of crystals dissolved, the greater the solubility of
the compound.

④ Only comment on what the data tells you – nothing else!
⑤ Look for where the lines cross... and remember the units!
⑥ Answer = Mass of Crystals Dissolved at 70°C – Mass of Crystals
Dissolved at 30°C. Remember to show your working!

Analysis – the examination of something by breaking it down and identifying the separate parts

Atomic mass – the average mass (in atomic mass units) of the isotopes of an element

Calorie – a unit of heat energy – the energy required to raise the temperature of 1g of water by 1°C

Calorimetry – the measurement of quantities of heat energy

Distillation – the process of boiling a liquid and condensing its vapours

Electronic structure – the arrangement of electrons within an atom

Empirical formula – shows the ratio of elements in a compound

Group – a vertical column of elements in the periodic table

Hard water – water containing salts which prevent soap from lathering

Joule – a unit of energy and work

Period – a horizontal row of elements in the periodic table

Saturated solution – a solution which will not dissolve any more solute at a particular temperature

Solubility curve – graph which shows how the solubility of a solute changes with temperature

Titration – chemical analysis used to determine the concentration of a known reactant

Transition elements – block of metallic elements in the middle of the periodic table

How Science Works Key Words

Here are the words that might be used in your exam, with a definition so you know exactly what you are being asked.

Accuracy – how correct or exact something is. The more times you repeat an experiment, the closer the average value (mean) of the results will be to the true value.

Analyse – look at in detail

Apply – relate to, put to practical use

Calculate – work out

Consider – think about

Construct – make, put together

Contrast – look at the differences between

Describe – put into words

Determine – decide, conclude

Discuss – talk about

Evaluate – determine the worth of

Evidence – results of an experiment or facts that you can use to prove or disprove a theory

Explain – put into words

Fair test – a test where conditions are controlled so no factors other than the one you are changing / controlling have an effect on what is being measured

Impact (social, economic, environmental) – an effect

Informed judgements – a balanced view based on information

Interpret – explain the meaning of

Precision – exactness, only a small spread / range of results

Predict – make a good guess at what you expect to happen

Recognise – notice, accept or be aware of

Relate – make a connection to something (like a real life situation or other experiments, etc.)

Reliability – dependability of the results, based on how accurate the measuring instruments are

Sketch – a drawing

Suggest reasons for – think of possible reasons for

Theory – an idea about what will happen

Variables – something that changes during the course of an investigation

Independent variable – the variable you change and have control over

Dependent variable – the variable (output) you measure

Index

Periodic Table

Key

| relative atomic mass |
| **atomic symbol** |
| name |
| atomic (proton) number |

| 1 | H hydrogen 1 |

Group 1	Group 2											Group 3	Group 4	Group 5	Group 6	Group 7	Group 0
																	4 He helium 2
7 Li lithium 3	9 Be beryllium 4											11 B boron 5	12 C carbon 6	14 N nitrogen 7	16 O oxygen 8	19 F fluorine 9	20 Ne neon 10
23 Na sodium 11	24 Mg magnesium 12											27 Al aluminium 13	28 Si silicon 14	31 P phosphorus 15	32 S sulfur 16	35.5 Cl chlorine 17	40 Ar argon 18
39 K potassium 19	40 Ca calcium 20	45 Sc scandium 21	48 Ti titanium 22	51 V vanadium 23	52 Cr chromium 24	55 Mn manganese 25	56 Fe iron 26	59 Co cobalt 27	59 Ni nickel 28	63.5 Cu copper 29	65 Zn zinc 30	70 Ga gallium 31	73 Ge germanium 32	75 As arsenic 33	79 Se selenium 34	80 Br bromine 35	84 Kr krypton 36
85 Rb rubidium 37	88 Sr strontium 38	89 Y yttrium 39	91 Zr zirconium 40	93 Nb niobium 41	96 Mo molybdenum 42	[98] Tc technetium 43	101 Ru ruthenium 44	103 Rh rhodium 45	106 Pd palladium 46	108 Ag silver 47	112 Cd cadmium 48	115 In indium 49	119 Sn tin 50	122 Sb antimony 51	128 Te tellurium 52	127 I iodine 53	131 Xe xenon 54
133 Cs caesium 55	137 Ba barium 56	139 La* lanthanum 57	178 Hf hafnium 72	181 Ta tantalum 73	184 W tungsten 74	186 Re rhenium 75	190 Os osmium 76	192 Ir iridium 77	195 Pt platinum 78	197 Au gold 79	201 Hg mercury 80	204 Tl thallium 81	207 Pb lead 82	209 Bi bismuth 83	[209] Po polonium 84	[210] At astatine 85	[222] Rn radon 86
[223] Fr francium 87	[226] Ra radium 88	[227] Ac* actinium 89	[261] Rf rutherfordium 104	[262] Db dubnium 105	[266] Sg seaborgium 106	[264] Bh bohrium 107	[277] Hs hassium 108	[268] Mt meitnerium 109	[271] Ds darmstadtium 110	[272] Rg roentgenium 111							

Elements with atomic numbers 112–116 have been reported but not fully authenticated

*The Lanthanides (atomic numbers 58–71) and the Actinides (atomic numbers 90–103) have been omitted.

Cu and **Cl** have not been rounded to the nearest whole number.